D0831106

NATIONAL CANNERS ASSOCIATION
RESEARCH LABORATORIES

E. J. CAMERON, *Director,* Washington, D. C.

J. RUSSELL ESTY, *Director,* San Francisco, California

CANNED FOODS
IN HUMAN NUTRITION

National Canners Association,
Washington, D. C.
1950

COPYRIGHT

NATIONAL CANNERS ASSOCIATION

1950

BOARD OF EDITORS

Editors

E. J. CAMERON
J. RUSSELL ESTY

Associate Editors

E. D. CLARK   L. E. CLIFCORN   J. F. FEASTER

Editorial Associates

O. R. ALEXANDER   F. C. LAMB
D. G. HEBERLEIN   K. H. MONROE
MARGARET IVES   K. R. SMITH
        M. D. TOMPKINS

This Seal denotes that the manuscript of this publication has been reviewed by the Council on Foods and Nutrition of the American Medical Association, prior to its printing, and is acceptable to the Council.

FOREWORD

The mysteries of life are fascinating to explore. And there is no reason to believe that even the simplest living organism —much less a human body—will be fully understood in the immediate future. Meanwhile, everyone is faced with the necessity—and it is generally a pleasant prospect—of eating to preserve normal health and activity. Each advance in understanding the nature of food or its manner of functioning inside living cells has a remarkably consistent record of becoming useful.

The intensive study of food composition and retention of nutritive quality during processing and storage of canned foods, sponsored jointly by the National Canners Association and the Can Manufacturers Institute, constitutes an outstanding service to the public as well as to food manufacturers.

It is without doubt a great accomplishment to make available the world over a safe, attractive, reasonably stable, low cost supply of foods in great variety. But it is a more difficult and more valuable contribution to furnish foods that meet the body's requirements for health. Leaders in the canned foods industry merit commendation for the thoroughness and vigor with which they have tackled the problem of bringing modern progress in the science of nutrition to the consumer's dinner table.

Studies such as reported in the present publication would not have been possible except on the basis of research to discover, measure and appraise the health significance of the great variety of nutrients that characterize common foods. The initiative shown by the industry in its cooperative study augurs equally well for continued economic success and protection of public health.

C. G. KING
Scientific Director, Nutrition Foundation, Inc.
and Professor of Chemistry, Columbia University

INTRODUCTION

The purpose of this bulletin is to provide a convenient and authoritative reference source on the nutritive values of commercially canned foods, their proper handling and preparation for use by the ultimate consumer, and their practical applications in meeting the optimum requirements of human nutrition.

Commercially canned foods were among the first studied after the modern era of nutrition research began in the United States. In 1922, the National Canners Association published its first edition of Bulletin 19-L "Vitamins in Canned Foods" in which were collected the findings made in these early researches. Recognizing the growing importance of nutrition research on the products of the canning industry, in 1923 the Association entered into a collaborative program of investigation with the Teachers College of Columbia University which extended through 1936 and culminated with the issue of the Fourth Revised Edition of Bulletin 19-L in December, 1937. During this period, considerable contributions to knowledge of the nutritional values of canned foods were also made by institutional, industrial, and State and Federal laboratories or agencies.

In 1942, owing to the war-time demand and necessity for more complete information on nutrients in canned foods, the current nutrition program jointly sponsored by the National Canners Association and the Can Manufacturers Institute was inaugurated. Over the past several years, the findings made by the universities and colleges cooperating in this program have greatly extended existing knowledge of the nutritive contributions of canned foods and have, to a great extent, made possible the publication of this bulletin. It is hoped that the information contained in these pages may lead to improved understanding and usage of commercially canned foods.

In presenting this bulletin, appreciation is expressed to those members of the research staffs of the American Can

Company and the Continental Can Company, Inc., and of the laboratories of the National Canners Association who have served on the Board of Editors. Without the cooperative efforts of these groups of scientists, the preparation of this bulletin would hardly have been possible.

Special acknowledgment is due R. W. Pilcher, Associate Director of Research, American Can Company, who is to be credited with the major part of the initial planning of the bulletin and to Franklin C. Bing, who gave freely from his wide editorial experience. Acknowledgment is also due C. A. Greenleaf and H. K. Wilder, of the National Canners Association, and R. E. Henry and G. T. Peterson, of the Continental Can Company, Inc., for their assistance in the preparation of the final manuscript.

CARLOS CAMPBELL,
Secretary, National Canners Association.

TABLE OF CONTENTS

9

PAGE

LIST OF ILLUSTRATIONS

Section I

MODERN CONCEPTS OF NUTRITION

HISTORY OF THE ESSENTIAL NUTRIENTS

It has, of course, always been known that the body needs food, and that man must eat to live. Nutrition is the science of foods and their relation to health. It is built on a considerable fund of information about the components of foodstuffs and how they are altered in processing, storage, preparation for the table, and how they are transformed chemically in the body, both in health and disease. The science of nutrition has for its ultimate goal the development and maintenance of strong, sturdy bodies. It has for an immediate objective the determination of what components of foods are needed for health and how much of each dietary essential is required for the growth of infants, children, and adolescents, for the special demands of pregnancy and lactation, and for the particular problems encountered in the feeding of persons in old age or in sickness.

The late Professor Mendel, a distinguished scientist who devoted a lifetime of study to this field, once summed up the scope of nutrition in the title of a book (1). It was called "Nutrition: The Chemistry of Life".

The Beginnings of the Science of Nutrition

The history of this science is intimately associated with the development of chemistry and other sciences (2-6). These have an ancient history. But just as modern chemistry may be said to have been initiated with the quantitative work of Lavoisier on the nature of oxidation, so also may it be said that the modern science of nutrition was simultaneously begun with the studies of Lavoisier on oxidations within the human body. He expounded a theory of the consumption of oxygen and the evolution of carbon dioxide by animals, and this

Home of the National Canners Association in Washington, D. C.

theory still holds true. His theory was that "Respiration is only a slow combustion of carbon and hydrogen and animals are true combustible bodies which burn and consume themselves." Of course, it is now known that the story of oxidations involves many complicated reactions before carbon and hydrogen, as they are found in foods, are burned to carbon dioxide and water in the tissues to yield heat and energy to the body. The carbon dioxide is eliminated chiefly by way of the lungs; the water is eliminated partly through the lungs, and also through the skin and the kidneys.

Nitrogen is another important element of foods, in addition to the carbon and hydrogen with which the experiments of Lavoisier were concerned. The Dutch chemist Mülder in 1838 characterized the principal nitrogen components of plant and animal tissues and selected the name "protein" for them; the word comes from a Greek root which means "first" and appropriately indicated Mülder's belief that these nitrogenous materials were of prime importance to living organisms. The end-product of the metabolism, or chemical changes within the body, of the nitrogen of proteins, is urea. This is a solid crystalline substance that is eliminated in solution by way of the kidneys.

Lavoisier's important and fundamental investigations were performed in the last years before his death by the guillotine during the French revolution, in 1794. It was about that time that the use of cow's milk in the artificial feeding of infants was gaining a foothold in medical circles. Not many years later, in 1810, another Frenchman, Nicholas Appert by name was developing a method of preserving foods by heating, thus laying the foundation of the modern canning industry. It is more than a coincidence that commercial canning, modern chemistry, and the science of nutrition experienced a contemporaneous development. The technology of canning foods has its basis in chemistry, bacteriology, and related sciences.

The English chemist, William Prout, in 1834, distinguished several different kinds of nutrients in foods. These he called the saccharine, oleaginous, and albuminous groups. Today these would be termed the carbohydrates, fats, and proteins, and they are the substances which make up the bulk of the solid substance of foods and body tissues. The pioneer investigators of the nineteenth century showed that these components of foods could be digested by enzymes of the intestinal juices and, after absorption into the blood, undergo numerous transformations before they were ultimately oxidized or stored in the tissues. Claude Bernard, the distinguished physiologist, studied the amount of sugar in the blood going to and away from the liver, and proved that the liver could store D-glucose, the sugar of the blood, in the form of glycogen, or animal starch, and glycogen could be reconverted into D-glucose. The Munich school of physiologists, under the leadership of Carl Voit, showed with geese that carbohydrates could be transformed into fats in the body. It was demonstrated also that muscles could do work at the expense of carbohydrate or fat, and part of the protein in food could be converted into carbohydrate. These were some of the leading discoveries in nutrition prior to 1890.

The mobile laboratory of the National Canners Association is equipped for chemical and bacteriological control work in canning production. Manned by a staff of technologists, this mobile unit brings to canners the facilities of modern technology.

Along with mineral salts and water it was long believed that the important components of foods were the carbohydrates, fats, and proteins. The remarkably accurate metabolism experiments of Atwater and his associates seemed to emphasize in a quantitative way the correctness of this belief. In 1895, these American investigators showed that the law of conservation of energy is applicable to man. The calories of foods, less those of the excreta, equalled the heat and energy output of a man in health, who was maintaining body weight. The calories, or units of heat produced in the oxidation of foods, were derived entirely from the combustion of carbohydrates, fats, and proteins, within limits of accuracy of the determinations in the laboratory.

Tables of food values for many years emphasized the caloric view of nutrition. According to this view foods were of value largely because of the number of calories they could provide. This was before the significance of the vitamins became known.

The Vitamins

The vitamins had been discovered earlier, but not until after World War I did their full significance come to be generally realized. Certain deficiency diseases had long been known to result from the prolonged consumption of restricted diets, and to be cured by the feeding of certain foods, but not alleviated by the administration of available medicines. As early as 1665 Dietz successfully used French horseradish sauce to reduce the incidence of scurvy in sailors on long voyages. James Lind in 1757, showed that scurvy could be successfully treated by giving the patients lime or lemon juice. The practice of giving limes to British sailors for the prevention of scurvy later became a required practice; this practice led to the nickname of "Limeys" by which British sailors are still commonly known. In the 19th century a Japanese physician, Takaki, showed that the disease called beriberi, which developed in sailors whose diet aboard ship contained much polished rice, could be prevented by substituting brown rice. Other deficiency diseases, such as pellagra, which was described by Casal before 1800, were known to be associated with a deficient diet, but their precise connection with specific foods had not been worked out. Rickets was another deficiency disease, long known, but of uncertain etiology. It was not until comparatively recent years that the relationship between vitamins and dietary deficiency diseases became known.

The vitamins first came to scientific attention when investigators reported failure of animals to thrive when fed mixtures of purified protein, carbohydrate, fat, and mineral salt mixtures patterned after the composition of the salts of milk. Lunin, in 1881, fed such a diet to adult mice and found that the animals lost weight and died within a month. When fed on milk the animals could live for long periods of time in apparent health. In reporting these observations Lunin suggested "There is something in milk besides the casein, fat, lactose, and mineral salts—a substance that is indispensable for nutrition." Other workers obtained similar results. Hopkins, in 1906, reported that laboratory rats maintained on a diet of isolated foodstuffs would thrive for a time if a small amount of cow's milk was added to the diet. He postulated the existence of "accessory factors" in foods which were not protein, fat, or carbohydrate, and which were essential for growth. In 1912 Funk, at the Lister Institute in London, was able to obtain a water extract from rice polishings which alleviated the polyneuritis of animals maintained on a diet of polished rice. On analysis it appeared to be an amino compound, so he called his substance a "vitamine" meaning an amine which was essential for life. Working independently, Hart, Steenbock, and McCollum at the University of Wisconsin, and Osborne and Mendel at Yale University found that laboratory animals failed to grow on so-called synthetic diets unless small amounts of butterfat were added to the diet. The fat-soluble factor, which was shown to be present in butterfat, egg yolk, and cod liver oil, but to be absent from many other fats, was called "fat-soluble A" by McCollum, and Funk's antineuritic factor was called "water-soluble B". Later, at the suggestion of Drummond, the terminal "e" was dropped from the word "vitamine" and the term "vitamin" became accepted as a general designation for all accessory food substances.

Important sources of vitamin B were brewers' yeast and liver. As investigations continued after World War I other water-soluble factors were found in these natural foodstuffs and in others, which were important in nutrition.

In 1922, Kohman published the first review issued by the National Canners Association on vitamins in canned foods. It is of interest to note the status of knowledge at that time as indicated by the following statement in that Bulletin:

> "It is now universally agreed that there are at least three vitamins, all of which are necessary in the human diet. Their complete role in nutrition is still far from clear. Each vitamin may consist of two or more substances of similar properties and physiological functions. There is some evidence in favor of the argument that at least vitamins A and B are not single substances, though no one is willing at present definitely to commit himself to that belief."

At the time when Kohman wrote this account vitamin A and the factor later designated vitamin D were often confused, because both are fat-soluble factors, and both are found in cod liver oil. It was subsequently found, by heating cod liver oil while bubbling air through it, that the vitamin A activity could be destroyed, leaving a material which still retained anti-rachitic properties. Thus vitamins A and D became differentiated. It was not until several years later that the multiple nature of vitamin B in such products as brewers' yeast and liver was demonstrated; these components of the B complex were designated vitamins B_1 and B_2. From this time on progress was rapid. In 1948 vitamin B_{12} was isolated.

The letter C had been given to a water-soluble factor which was effective in the treatment of scurvy. By means of feeding experiments which extended over long periods of time, a fat-soluble factor important in the prevention of sterility in rats was discovered and called vitamin E.

Thus, by 1925 there were five vitamins that had been fairly well characterized by biological studies with animals. These were known as vitamins A, B, C, D, and E. Of these vitamins, A, D, and E were fat-soluble, and B and C were water-soluble factors.

Only a few of the highlights in the history of the advancement of nutritional knowledge have been indicated in this brief review, but more extensive chronological histories may be found in the following publications (2-5).

Recent Developments

In the last 25 years there has been a tremendous increase in knowledge about not only the vitamins but about other factors in foods which are of importance to health. Many more vitamins have been described than there are letters in the alphabet. Only a comparatively few of these factors have been shown to be of significance in the practical feeding of people.

The principal lines of development in research which led to the present knowledge of the vitamins may be summarized in the following manner:

1. The number of vitamins in foods, as shown by suitable feeding experiments, and in particular by work with microorganisms as well as with various species of laboratory animals, has been greatly expanded. There is evidence that not all of the dietary essentials have been discovered. While the vitamins now known are large in number, their significance in human nutrition has not been completely worked out in many instances. New vistas of unexplored realms seem to be making an appearance with each new contribution from laboratory and clinic.

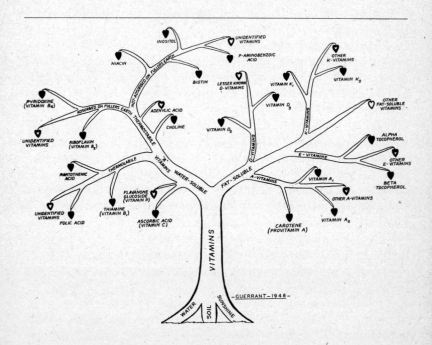

The "Vitamin Tree", supplied by courtesy of Professor N. B. Guerrant, of Pennsylvania State College, shows the many vitamins on the tree of research. Some of the vitamins, it will be noted, had not been fully "ripened" when the chart was prepared in 1948. Notable by its absence, for example, is vitamin B₁₂ which was isolated in 1949.

2. Isolation and synthesis of many of the vitamins have been accomplished. This was a noteworthy development of the period from about 1930 to 1940, and later.

3. Further understanding of the functions of the vitamins in the body, and their relationships with other factors, has been obtained.

4. Improved methods for the quantitative estimation of the vitamins in foods and in body fluids have been developed.

Coincident with this new quantitative era in the use of the vitamins came a demand for more precise analytical data about the vitamin content of foods, and the effects of processing on these factors.

Progress in other fields of nutrition has been equally rapid in the last 25 years. The biochemistry of proteins has become to a large extent the biochemistry of the amino acids, the products into which the proteins are converted by the actions of the digestive juices. A clearer understanding is now available of the intermediary metabolism of amino acids, carbohydrates and fats, and their interrelationships with vitamins and other factors. Certain unsaturated fatty acids, obtained by the digestion of fats, are known to be important in the nutrition of laboratory animals, and there is some evidence that they may be important in human nutrition as well. Finally, the field of mineral nutrition has been developed to the point that some of the hitherto unknown functions of a number of the elements, present in traces in foods, are understood, and a clear understanding of the quantitative requirements of the major inorganic elements is at hand.

The dietary components which are known to be important in human and animal physiology are indicated in Table 1. Future research may lead to the inclusion of still other factors in such a list. The factors which require consideration in the planning of dietaries are the subjects of the following chapters.

TABLE 1

Food Factors of Importance in Human Nutrition

Factors recognized in 1925	Additional factors recognized in 1950
Proteins (Probable essentiality of some amino acids)	Essentiality of amino acids: Threonine, Valine, Leucine, Isoleucine
Carbohydrates	Lysine, Methionine, Phenylalanine
Fats	Tryptophan
Mineral Salts: Calcium, Magnesium, Sodium, Potassium, Phosphorus, Chlorine, Sulfur, Iron, Iodine	Essentiality of unsaturated fatty acids: Linoleic, linolenic and arachidonic acids. Essentiality of certain trace elements: Cobalt, Copper, Fluorine, Manganese, Zinc
Vitamins: A, B, C, D, E	Additional vitamins: Riboflavin, Niacin, Niacinamide, Pyridoxine, Pantothentic acid, Inositol, Biotin, Choline, Vitamin B_{12}
Calories (from oxidation of proteins, carbohydrates and fats)	Folic acid, Vitamin K
Roughage	(Relationship of carotene to vitamin A, identification of thiamine as the antineuritic factor, identification of the tocopherols as vitamin E)
Water	Para-amino benzoic acid

REFERENCES

1. Mendel, L. B. *Nutrition: The Chemistry of Life.* Yale University Press, New Haven, 1925.

2. McCollum, E. V., Orent-Keiles, E., and Day, H. G. *The Newer Knowledge of Nutrition, 5th Ed.* The Macmillan Company, New York, 1939.

3. Dutcher, R. A. and Haley, D. E. *Introduction to Agricultural Biochemistry.* John Wiley and Sons, Inc., New York, 1932.

4. Sherman, H. C. *Chemistry of Food and Nutrition, 7th Ed.* The Macmillan Company, New York, 1946.

5. Rosenberg, H. R. *Chemistry and Physiology of the Vitamins.* Interscience Publishers, Inc., New York, 1942.

6. United States Department of Agriculture, *Food and Life, Yearbook of Agriculture 1939.* U. S. Gov't. Printing Office, Washington, D. C., 1939.

Chapter 2

THE DIETARY REQUIREMENTS OF MAN

In order to put information about the dietary essentials to use it is necessary to know not only what components of the diet are essential but also how much of each is needed. Many investigators have devoted considerable study to this problem (1). Much painstaking labor is required to perform the type of study needed to obtain the data on which a judgment may be based.

In many respects accounts of the dietary requirements bear a resemblance to the balance sheets of financial reports. They are not light reading for an idle moment, but they provide working data of extraordinary importance to persons trained to interpret and utilize the information wisely. Information about the dietary requirements is fundamental to every sound nutrition program. Such information provides the basis for intelligent rationing of foods during wartime. Questions about the fat requirement for the health of civilians gained prominence when fats were scarce. Questions of the water requirements of man assumed special significance when calculations had to be made of the needs for troops engaged in desert warfare. Fortunately, the data needed to answer these and similar questions with reasonable exactness were available when they arose during World War II.

Early Work

It was early recognized that protein was essential in the diet, and Carl Voit as long ago as 1881 reported an attempt to determine how much protein was required. From analyses of the diets of German soldiers he obtained figures of the actual food consumption in terms of the known nutrients.

27

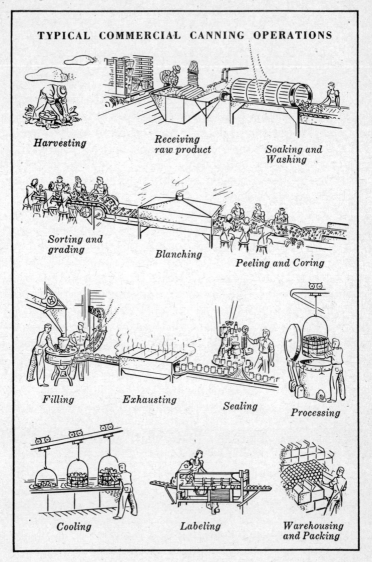

TYPICAL COMMERCIAL CANNING OPERATIONS

Harvesting

Receiving raw product

Soaking and Washing

Sorting and grading

Blanching

Peeling and Coring

Filling

Exhausting

Sealing

Processing

Cooling

Labeling

Warehousing and Packing

Courtesy American Can Company

From these data he considered that an adult man of average weight (70 to 75 kilograms; 154 to 165 pounds) doing muscular work should have an allowance of 118 grams of protein, and about 3000 calories. These calories would be supplied by the protein plus 56 grams of fat and 500 grams of carbohydrate.

With other groups, and particularly in other countries, different values were observed, and widely different ideas prevailed about the actual amount of protein desirable for maintenance of health. Many experiments were planned to secure a better estimate of the requirement; for it was recognized that a figure obtained from the determination of the protein content of the average diet was only an indication of what was customary with the food habits of the group considered.

Balance studies on human beings thus were conceived and performed, usually on a few young adults, and most often on students or the investigators themselves. A diet would be selected, consumed regularly in measured quantities, and the nitrogen output of the body determined. Careful records would be made of body weight, and these records together with data on the physical examination of the subjects and records of their subjective impressions, were useful in the interpretation of the data. Refinements might be introduced, such as the control of minor nitrogen losses through the skin or by channels other than the kidneys and the intestines. The principle involved was that if the nitrogen losses equalled the nitrogen intake, then the body was in equilibrium, neither gaining nor losing protein, and the protein requirement of the person was being met, under the conditions of the experiment. If the output of nitrogen exceeded the intake, the body was said to be in negative balance, which meant that protein was being lost from the body tissues, and the intake was considered insufficient.

Many of the data on adult human requirements for the various nutrients have been obtained by such balance studies, in which the intake of one nutrient was varied and the amount determined which was just sufficient to maintain equilibrium or to permit a slight positive balance. With growing children the determination of the requirement is more difficult. Not only must a positive balance be obtained, because the growing body is building tissue, but the rate of growth and physical well-being should be adequate.

Professor H. C. Sherman in particular has employed the balance type of experiment extensively to determine the requirements for protein, calcium, phosphorous and iron. With these nutrients he early reached the decision that it would be well to add a margin of safety to the experimentally determined requirement for equilibrium of adults. Usually this additional amount was fifty per cent above the experimentally determined value.

For the vitamins it has been necessary as a rule to employ special methods of arriving at an estimate of the requirements. In the case of thiamine and riboflavin—two members of what has been called the vitamin B complex—methods are employed which involve the determination of the urinary excretion of the vitamin on different levels of intake. It is found that a direct relationship exists between intake and excretion at various high levels of intake, but at lower levels a point is reached where further reduction in intake has little effect on the amount excreted. The interpretaton given to this phenomenon is that at the higher levels the intake is in excess of the requirement, and the excess is excreted, while at lower levels of intake the tissues tend to give up their supply of the essential nutrient, which is needed for body functions. When graphs of intakes and excretions are plotted a break in the curve occurs, and this point is considered to be where the intake is just sufficient to maintain normal tissue concentration. Other special technics have been found useful, such as the estimation of the probable vitamin A requirement by determinations of the quantity of vitamin A needed to give normal dark adaptation of the eye of subjects who have been depleted of their stores of this factor. Vitamin D requirements have been measured not only by determining the amount needed to prevent rickets in infants, but also by determining the amount needed for maximum retention of calcium. Requirements may be expected to differ as a result of differences in age, sex, weight, state of health, bodily activity, and other factors, such as the method employed in making the determinations.

The Evaluation of Experimental Data on Dietary Requirements

It has been stated that dietary standards are necessary for:

1. The evaluation of diets consumed or planned, in order to answer the question: Is the food intake adequate nutritionally?

2. The evaluation of an individual food, in order to answer the question: Is a food article a rich, fair, or negligible source of a dietary essential?

Whenever scientific workers meet to discuss questions of this nature it is inevitable that consideration be given to dietary standards.

When the White House Conference on Child Health and Protection met in 1930, questions of the dietary needs of children received much attention (2). Valuable unpublished data were made available about the caloric requirements of growing children, and consideration was given to published data about several other components of the diet which were known to be essential at the time. Several years later, when the members of the League of Nations Health Committee studied the problem of nutrition in different countries they had to consider the question of dietary requirements (3). Standards were adopted which were largely those in use by Mary Swartz Rose, a member of the Committee, and for many years a leading student of human nutrition. The most widely used standards today are those of the Food and Nutrition Board of the National Research Council. These standards are known as the recommended daily dietary allowances. They are particularly valuable because of the large number of persons who participated in their development, as well as in the manner in which judgments were reached.

The Recommended Daily Dietary Allowances

The present Food and Nutrition Board met in October, 1940, as a Committee on Food and Nutrition of the National Research Council. A problem for consideration before the committee was a request from the Surgeon General of the U.S. Army for an opinion about the suitability of a formula proposed for a multi-vitamin capsule intended as a dietary supplement for certain military personnel. Was it a suitable formula? To answer this question it was necessary to reach some agreement as to the dietary needs for the vitamins. This task was assigned by the Chairman to a small subcommittee. Thus, what came to be the Committee on Dietary Allowances was begun. This Committee is still functioning, though with different personnel.

The first published report of the Committee appeared in January, 1943 (4). In 1944 additional material was added (5) and, in August, 1945, a second edition was published in which some revisions of allowances were made as a result of further information. The third or 1948 edition is the latest, and it contained still more revisions (6). The table of dietary allowances from the report of the Committee is reproduced as Table 2. This table shows the recommended daily allowance for different age groups of both sexes for ten of the dietary essentials.

Those persons who use the table are urged to give consideration also to the explanations provided in the footnotes and text of the report. These explanations are paraphrased or quoted in the following paragraphs, in order to present an orderly discussion of the subject in the present bulletin.

The ten dietary essentials which the committee found could be stated in quantitative terms of requirements are: Calories,

TABLE 2

Recommended Daily Dietary Allowances
Revised 1948

After: Food and Nutrition Board, National Research Council (6)

	Calories	Protein gm.	Calcium gm.	Iron mg.	Vitamin A, I.U.	Thiamine, mg.	Riboflavin, mg.	Niacin (Nicotinic acid) mg.	Ascorbic acid, mg.	Vitamin D, I.U.
Man (154 lb., 70 kg.)										
Sedentary	2400	70	1.0	12	5000	1.2	1.8	12	75	..
Physically active	3000	70	1.0	12	5000	1.5	1.8	15	75	..
With heavy work	4500	70	1.0	12	5000	1.8	1.8	18	75	..
Woman (123 lb., 56 kg.)										
Sedentary	2000	60	1.0	12	5000	1.0	1.5	10	70	..
Moderately active	2400	60	1.0	12	5000	1.2	1.5	12	70	..
Very active	3000	60	1.0	12	5000	1.5	1.5	15	70	..
Pregnancy (latter half)	2400	85	1.5	15	6000	1.5	2.5	15	100	400
Lactation	3000	100	2.0	15	8000	1.5	3.0	15	150	400
Children up to 12 yrs.										
Under 1 yr.	*	†	1.0	6	1500	0.4	0.6	4	30	400
1-3 yrs. (27 lb., 12 kg.)	1200	40	1.0	7	2000	0.6	0.9	6	35	400
4-6 yrs. (42 lb., 19 kg.)	1600	50	1.0	8	2500	0.8	1.2	8	50	400
7-9 yrs. (58 lb., 26 kg.)	2000	60	1.0	10	3500	1.0	1.5	10	60	400
10-12 yrs. (78 lb., 35 kg.)	2500	70	1.2	12	4500	1.2	1.8	12	75	400
Children over 12 yrs.										
Girls, 13-15 yrs. (108 lb., 49 kg.)	2600	80	1.3	15	5000	1.3	2.0	13	80	400
Girls, 16-20 yrs. (122 lb., 55 kg.)	2400	75	1.0	15	5000	1.2	1.8	12	80	400
Boys, 13-15 yrs. (108 lb., 49 kg.)	3200	85	1.4	15	5000	1.5	2.0	15	90	400
Boys, 16-20 yrs. (141 lb., 64 kg.)	3800	100	1.4	15	6000	1.7	2.5	17	100	400

* 110/2.2 lb. (1 kg.).
† 3.5/2.2 lb. (1 kg.).

protein, calcium, iron, vitamin A, thiamine, riboflavin, niacin, ascorbic acid and vitamin D. In addition, recommendations were also included in the report about the following factors: Fat, iodine, water, salt, phosphorus, copper, vitamin K, folic acid and other members of the vitamin B complex.

Calories—These are heat and food energy units obtained by the oxidation of protein, fat and carbohydrate. In calculating mixed foods or diets it is customary to consider that each gram of protein or carbohydrate yields 4 calories, and each gram of fat, 9 calories, when burned in the body. The caloric allowances must be adjusted to meet specific needs of an individual. Therefore, the values in the tables are group averages rather than the requirements of each person in the various groups indicated. The proper calorie allowance is that which over an extended period will maintain body weight of adults, or allow for a rate of growth of children which is "most conducive to well-being."

Protein—Proteins are needed by the body for the growth of new tissue and for the maintenance of the adult. In general, except for pregnancy and lactation, a standard of one gram of protein daily for each kilogram of body weight has been recommended. Pregnant and lactating women require more, as do children. The allowances are considered liberal enough so that differences in amino acid composition of individual foods in a satisfactory mixed diet, containing proteins of animal origin to a moderate degree, are not important. An infant fed human milk may thrive with an intake considerably less than the recommended allowances, because of the superior content of essential amino acids in human milk.

Calcium—Calcium is needed for the growth and development of bones and teeth, and in smaller amounts for the physiologic needs of the other body tissues and fluids. It is needed by the adult as well as by the growing child. The requirement for calcium is related to the body's intake of and need for phosphorus and vitamin D, although it is emphasized that vitamin D does not decrease the need for calcium.

Phosphorus—The table does not include detailed allowances for phosphorus, largely because this element is widely distributed in foods, no evidence of uncomplicated phosphorus deficiency in normal human beings has been reported, and because it can be assumed that when the protein and calcium needs are met, by the use of ordinary foods, the needs of phosphorus likewise will be met. An outstanding source of calcium is milk, which is also one of the best sources of phosphorus. If consideration must be given to phosphorus allowances, the Committee considers that for children, and for women in the latter part of pregnancy and during lactation, the allowance is at least equal to the allowance for calcium. For other adults the phosphorus allowance may be considered to be about 1.5 times that for calcium.

Phosphorus is needed because it is a component of all cells of the body, is needed for normal bone and tooth structure, and because compounds containing phosphorus participate in many of the physiologic activities of the cells, tissue and body fluids.

Vitamin D—This vitamin is needed for the prevention of rickets in growing children, and for normal metabolism of calcium and phosphorus in adolescents. The need for vitamin D by adults in vigorous health is probably minimal. "For persons working at night," states the report, "and for nuns and others whose habits shield them from sunlight, as well as for elderly persons, the ingestion of small amounts of vitamin D is desirable."

Iron—Iron is needed for the production of hemoglobin of the blood and, in lesser amounts, for the production of other iron compounds of the body. There is evidence that men need relatively little iron, considerably less than the amounts suggested.

Vitamin A—This vitamin is important in the maintenance of a healthy condition of the epithelial cells of the body. It is needed for normal dark adaptation of the eyes, a fact which permits one method of estimation of the vitamin A requirement. Vitamin A is present in many animal fats, such as those of liver, egg yolk, and milk. Many vegetables and fruits have vitamin A activity because the yellow pigments, the carotenes and cryptoxanthin which they contain, are converted into vitamin A in the body. The allowances are based on the assumption that about two-thirds of the vitamin A of the average diet of the United States is contributed by carotene, and that carotene has about half the biological value of vitamin A.

Thiamine—Thiamine or vitamin B_1 is needed as a component of enzymes of body cells which are concerned with the oxidation of carbohydrate. This vitamin prevents or cures beriberi, a dietary deficiency disease. The report points out that for adults receiving less than 2000 calories, as in reducing diets, the allowance for thiamine may be considered to be 1 milligram.

Riboflavin—Riboflavin is another member of the vitamin B complex sometimes called vitamin B_2. It is needed as a component of several oxidative enzymes of the body cells.

Niacin—Niacin is still another component of the vitamin B complex. It is present as a component of certain enzyme systems concerned with cellular respiration. It is the principal factor involved in the deficiency disease, pellagra, which however is usually complicated by deficiency of other food factors as well. The report points out that when the diet of the adult supplies less than 2000 calories, the allowance of niacin may be considered to be 10 milligrams.

Other B complex factors—Other components of the vitamin B complex doubtless are significant in human nutrition, but quantitative data about their requirements are not available. In general, it is considered that foods which supply adequate amounts of thiamine, riboflavin and niacin will tend to supply sufficient quantities of the remaining vitamins of the B complex.

Vitamin C—Ascorbic acid, or vitamin C as it was called before its chemical nature was determined, is necessary for the formation of the organic portion of bone and tooth structure, and other tissues of the body. It prevents or cures the deficiency disease, scurvy. It is needed for normal health at all ages.

Fat—Fat allowances are based on food habits rather than on precise knowledge of the requirement, which has not been established. Experimental work with animals has demonstrated the necessity for certain unsaturated fatty acids present in natural fats (linoleic, linolenic and arachidonic acids) but the human needs, if any, for these fat components are not known. The report suggests that fat be included in the diet to the extent of at least 20 or 25 per cent of the total calories, and that the fat contain essential fatty acids to the extent of at least 1 per cent of the total calories. For children, adolescent persons, and adults consuming 4500 calories or more, it is desirable that from 30 to 35 per cent of the total calories be derived from fat. The report states, "Since foodstuffs such as meat, milk, cheese, nuts, etc., contribute fat to the diet, it is necessary to use separated or 'visible' fats such as butter, oleomargarine, lard, or shortenings to supply only one-third to one-half the [total] amounts [of fat] indicated."

Salt and Water—The requirements for salt and water are closely related. About 5 grams daily constitute a suitable allowance of salt for adults, except when there is profuse sweating, when more is needed.

A suitable allowance of water for adults is 2.5 liters daily, or about 1 milliliter for each calorie of food. This water may be in part a component of the foods which are consumed. At work or in hot environments the water requirement may reach as much as from 5 to 13 liters daily. "Water should be allowed *ad libitum,* since sensation of thirst usually serves as adequate guide to intake except for infants and sick persons."

When the intake of water is more than 4 liters daily one additional gram of salt for each additional liter of water should be allowed. "With heavy work or in hot climate 20 to 30 grams daily (of salt) may be consumed with meals and in drinking water. Even then, most persons do not need more salt than usually occurs in prepared foods. It has been shown that after acclimatization persons produce sweat that contains only about 0.5 gram to the liter in contrast with a content of 2 to 3 grams for sweat of the unacclimatized person. Consequently after acclimatization, need for increase of salt beyond that of ordinary food disappears."

Iodine—The Board has concluded that "the requirement for iodine is small, probably about 0.002 to 0.004 mg. daily for each kilogram of body weight, or a total of 0.15 to 0.30 mg. daily for the adult. This need is met by the regular use of iodized salt; its use is especially important in *adolescence* and *pregnancy*."

Copper—Copper is needed in order to enable the body to utilize iron for the production of hemoglobin. Adults need about 1 to 2 mg. of copper daily; children, about 0.05 mg. of copper for each kilogram of body weight. "A good diet normally will supply sufficient copper."

Vitamin K—Vitamin K is a fat-soluble factor needed for normal blood clotting. It is found in vegetables such as spinach, cabbages and cauliflower and, in lesser amounts, in other foods. Some vitamin K is produced by the action of bacteria in the intestine. It is usually supplied in suitable quantity by a good diet of ordinary foods. The exception is the unborn and newborn infant. For this reason supplemental vitamin K is recommended in the last month of pregnancy. "When it has not been given in this manner, it is recommended for the mother preceding delivery, or for the baby immediately after birth."

General Comments

In further explanation of its report the Committee emphasizes that the allowances are for a man weighing 70 kilograms (154 pounds), or a woman weighing 56 kilograms (123 pounds), and for children by age groups. It is emphasized that allowances for different age groups are for the middle of each age group, for average size and activity, and for persons in health. The allowances are for foods as eaten. The allowances are intended to serve as a guide in planning an adequate diet for all normal persons in a population group.

The allowances can not properly be used as the sole criterion of judging the state of nutrition of any population group. They can be used, however, as a guide for feeding population groups, when the data are weighted according to categories of age and sex.

Minimum Requirements

For some purposes minimum requirements may be needed rather than the more liberal recommended allowances. The minimum levels are those below which the diet should not be permitted to go for any extended periods of time. For short periods of emergency such levels may need to be considered as goals. This may be the case, for example, in relief feeding, or for some military purposes, for short periods of time.

An interesting development has been the establishment of minimum requirements for certain dietary essentials by the Food and Drug Administration (7). This was done as a result of public hearings at which testimony was offered, after which regulations were promulgated to serve as a guide in meeting the labeling requirements of food products intended for or recommended as products for special dietary use, as in the feeding of infants or the sick. These requirements are shown in Table 3.

An inspection of the values in the two tables reveals that the two sets of figures are close together in some instances. This may be taken as an indication that, for these dietary essentials, the experimental data are sufficiently extensive to permit general agreement about their interpretation. In the case of riboflavin the minimum requirement of the Food and Drug Administration is higher than the recommended allowance of the Food and Nutrition Board. Such was not the case in the first edition of the Food and Nutrition Board's publication. This fact may serve to indicate the lack of finality to many of the data in the difficult field of estimating the human requirement of the various food factors.

TABLE 3

Minimum Daily Requirements of Specific Nutrients as Required by the Food and Drug Administration for the Labeling of Foods for Special Dietary Uses

Adapted from: Federal Security Agency (7)

Nutrient	Infants	Children 1 to 5 yrs. inclusive	Children 6 to 11 yrs. inclusive	Children 12 yrs. and over	Adults
Vitamin A (U.S.P. units)..	1500	3000	3000	4000	4000
Thiamin (mg.)............	0.25	0.50	0.75	1	1
Ascorbic acid (mg.).......	10	20	20	30	30
Vitamin D (U.S.P. units)..	400	400	400	400	400
Riboflavin (mg.)	0.5	..	..	2.0	2.0
Calcium (g.)..............	..	0.75	0.75	0.75	0.75
Phosphorus (g.)...........	..	0.75	0.75	0.75	0.75
Iron (mg.)................	..	7.5	10	10	10

The iodine requirement is considered to be 0.1 mg. for a child or an adult. In the case of pregnant and lactating women the calcium and phosphorus requirements for labeling purposes, are considered to be 1.50 grams of each; while the iron requirements are considered to be 15.0 mg.

REFERENCES

1. Leitch, I. *The Evolution of Dietary Standards*. Nutrition Abstracts and Reviews 11, 509-521, 1942.
2. White House Conference on Child Health and Protection. *Growth and Development of the Child. Part III Nutrition*. The Century Company, New York, 1932.
3. League of Nations. *The Problem of Nutrition. II. Report on the Physiological Basis of Nutrition*. Ser. League of Nations Publication II-B-4, Geneva, 1936.
4. Food and Nutrition Board. *Recommended Dietary Allowances*. National Research Council Reprint and Circular Series No. 115, January, 1943.
5. Food and Nutrition Board. *Recommended Dietary Allowances*. National Research Council Reprint and Circular Series No. 122, August, 1945.
6. Food and Nutrition Board. *Recommended Dietary Allowances*. National Research Council Reprint and Circular Series No. 129, October, 1948.
7. Federal Security Agency, Food and Drug Administration. *Regulations Regarding the Labeling of Foods for Special Dietary Purposes*. Federal Register, November 22, 1941.

Chapter 3

MODERN NUTRITION PROGRAMS

So far the discussion has been concerned with the characterization of the nutritionally important substances in foods (Chapter 1) and with the requirements for nutritional well-being of persons in health, of each of the food components which need consideration in the planning of a satisfactory dietary (Chapter 2). In order to make practical use of this information it is necessary to know the composition of foods as consumed. With such information the physician can plan diet lists for patients, and the dietitian, nutritionist and home economist are in a position to provide intelligent supervision of menus or give satisfactory advice about meal planning.

The main portion of the present bulletin is devoted to a discussion of newer knowledge of the nutritional value of canned foods. Because of the wide variety of foods that are processed by the canning industry and the economy and ready availability of canned foods in all markets, it is believed that this information will be particularly helpful to all persons concerned with meal planning.

It is the purpose of the present chapter to discuss briefly the work of those professional bodies which are concerned with the practical application of the growing body of nutritional information. They are to an increasing degree responsible for the sound guidance of agricultural policies. Their views are important to all segments of the food industry, as well as to the general public.

Research on Foods and Nutrition

It is obvious that first the information about food needs must be obtained before anything can be done about meeting them in a rational manner. This investigative work is done in laboratories and in hospitals, usually connected with an educational or research institution. Programs of research need to be planned, supported, and arrangements made for them to be carried out by competent investigators. It is well for the results of experiments on human nutrition to be evaluated by others in a position to pass judgment on the data. Nutrition is an empirical science. There are many variables that can not be completely controlled and verification of striking results is highly desirable. Finally, information considered to be valid must be made available, first to the members of professional scientific groups, the physicians, dentists, nutritionists, dietitians, and home economists, and others who are in a position to advise the public or to apply the information directly in their professional activities. The last step, informing the public, demands the translation of scientific facts into simple, understandable terms. Professional persons, educators, science writers, food editors, advertising copy writers, and many other groups contribute to this phase of what in total constitutes a nutrition program for a community or a nation.

The food industry of the United States and Canada is playing a major part not only in helping in the acquisition of new knowledge but also in the dissemination of this information when acquired. Because of its size and importance in the national economy the canning industry has endeavored for many years to assume the responsibilities of leadership, along with other major food industries, in helping to stimulate further investigative work in pure science, and to acquire more and more information about its products, with the view to improving their nutritive quality whenever such action is indicated.

The Nutrition Foundation—To augment the work being done in nutrition research in existing institutions the food industry in December, 1941, developed an organization, the Nutrition Foundation, Inc., to provide working capital in support of basic research and education. The support of the

Nutrition Foundation comes from industry but its field of endeavor is entirely without immediate industry objectives. "There was clear recognition," it is stated in the Annual Report of the Scientific Director, (1) "that the program of the new organization should be wholly in the public interest and fundamental in character, in accord with the spirit and purpose of graduate schools and medical centers in leading universities."

The Foundation functions with the guidance of a Board of Trustees, a Scientific Advisory Committee, and a Food Industries Advisory Committee. The Scientific Advisory Committee which makes recommendations for grants in support of research is composed of fifteen outstanding investigators in the field of foods and nutrition. Grants to universities and similar institutions in the United States and Canada are made twice each year.

A total of $1,987,830.63 was appropriated for Grants-in-aid from July 1, 1942, to June 30, 1949, and was distributed in five areas of research as follows:

Area I.	Human Requirements of Individual Nutrients	$144,070.91
Area II.	Origin, Function and Measurement of Individual Nutrients	714,600.00
Area III.	Maternal and Infant Nutrition	196,800.00
Area IV.	Public Health Problems in Nutrition	485,450.00
Area V.	Education and Professional Training	269,119.72

The areas which are indicated and the sums which have been appropriated for studies in those areas are evidence of the broad scope of the investigations and their effective support.

Early recognition of the need for educational material about newer information obtained in this field induced the Foundation to sponsor since 1942 the publication of a monthly journal, "Nutrition Reviews". This publication aims to provide professional workers with interpretive articles describing current contributions of interest. The Foundation also distributes a leaflet for interested persons, entitled "Current

Research", which contains a selection of topics from each issue of "Nutrition Reviews" written in a less technical style. Science writers and food editors have found this leaflet to be an invaluable source of accurate information in the writing of articles for their readers. In this way information about newer developments in nutrition can be conveyed promptly to the reading public in all parts of the country.

It is through such activities, supplemented by those of individual companies and of associations, that the food industry is helping to fulfill its obligations to its customers, the consuming public. These activities augment those of a scientific and educational nature performed by other agencies.

Government Agencies and Nutrition

Among the organizations which currently and for many years have been active in the field of foods and nutrition are several government agencies (2). The U. S. Public Health Service for a long time has conducted investigations of the nutritional aspects of endemic diseases, notably in studies of pellagra, and more recently has been enabled to expand its facilities for programs of study of the medical aspects of nutrition and the training of health workers in nutrition. The Food and Drug Administration which, like the U. S. Public Health Service, is a division of the Federal Security Agency, exercises regulatory control over food products and their labeling, as provided for in the Federal Food, Drug and Cosmetic Act. There is a Division of Foods and a Division of Nutrition which, in addition to their regulatory activities, conduct investigative work on special problems in their fields. The Federal Trade Commission is another regulatory body which is concerned with the control of false advertising as an unfair trade practice. The U. S. Department of Agriculture, of course, is devoted to problems of food and agriculture and has many departments or bureaus concerned with different phases of its many activities. There has been Congressional support for the Department of Agriculture to investigate food and nutritional problems since 1894. The work on human nutrition in the agency since 1943 has been centered in the Bureau of Human Nutrition and Home Economics.

Bureau of Home Nutrition and Home Economics—In the field of nutrition the activities of the Bureau of Human Nutrition and Home Economics are broad (3). It studies the functions and metabolism of food and the nutritional requirements of human beings. Investigations are made of the interrelationships among the various nutrients necessary for physical well-being and of the effect of diet on nutritional status. Laboratory studies are made of the chemical composition and the nutritive value of foods in the raw state and after processing, such as cooking, canning, freezing, and storage—including, where necessary, the development and improvement of methods for such analyses.

General principles are developed for the home preparation and preservation of foods which are designed to result in wholesome palatable products of high nutritive value. Factors affecting palatability and consumer acceptance of various foods are investigated and evaluated. Recipes are developed for the home preparation of unusual or unfamiliar foods and new or modified recipes are developed for staple foods whenever their economic importance or a shift in food supply makes this desirable.

In the Bureau's economic studies, information is collected concerning the kinds and amounts of different foods consumed by people in various economic, occupational, and regional groups. These diets are then evaluated in order to suggest modifications that will promote the well-being of the population. Diet plans which are suited to nutritional needs of the people are developed and released. In planning these various diets the food habits, food supplies, and economic resources of the various population groups are taken into consideration.

The results of the activities of the Bureau are reported to the scientific world through technical papers and bulletins.

The research data are also translated into popular language and distributed through a variety of channels. The Bureau's bulletins, leaflets, charts, films and exhibits are brought to the attention of the public through the Extension Service, schools and colleges, magazines, the press, and the radio.

The Bureau conducts its research in food and nutrition both independently and in cooperation with such groups as the other bureaus of the Department of Agriculture, other Federal agencies, and state experiment stations. It also cooperates with other groups conducting research and educational programs designed to help families use their resources so as to obtain the best returns in health and other elements of satisfactory living.

While there is no centralized national nutrition agency in the United States the work of the major agencies in this field has been effectively coordinated through the Nutrition Programs Office of the Department of Agriculture (4). An interagency committee is made up of representatives of the U. S. Office of Education, the Children's Bureau, the American National Red Cross, the Farmers' Home Administration, the Extension Service, the Bureau of Human Nutrition and Home Economics, and the Public Health Service. All are government agencies with the exception of the Red Cross.

The interagency planning committee meets monthly to exchange information and to work toward the coordination of nutrition programs of the agencies on a national and state basis. Members of the committee plan their travel so as to function not only for their respective departments, but also act as consultants to nutrition committees which have been organized in the various states. The Nutrition Programs Office is in touch with the state committees directly and conferences with the state chairmen are held from time to time. It acts as a clearing house for information about the various state committees and issues "The Nutrition News Letter" each month covering the reports of committee activities.

This program is an educational one and no investigative work is included. However, the Bureau of Human Nutrition and Home Economics, which does engage in scientific research, develops subject matter for the program.

In addition to the interagency committee the Nutrition Programs Office meets occasionally with a broader interdepartmental committee when there is reason for the coordination of all government services in food and nutrition. Eight government agencies are represented, including several which engage directly in specialized nutrition research.

The recommendations for food selection included in the National Nutrition Program recognized seven classes of food products and specified the extent of usage. These basic seven food groups received wide distribution in chart form, such as that illustrated in Figure 1.

Other Non-Governmental Agencies

The Food and Nutrition Board of the National Research Council—This Board serves as a committee of experts on all phases of Nutrition, and acts in an advisory capacity in many broad nutrition programs (5). This is an independent organization which brings to bear unbiased scientific and medical opinion on problems of foods and nutrition, with regard solely to public welfare. It was established in 1940 by the National Research Council at the request of the National Defense Council, to advise with regard to the national nutrition programs. In 1941, because of expanding activities, this committee was redesignated as the Food and Nutrition Board, with a permanent secretarial force and an office for its executive secretary at 2101 Constitution Avenue, the home of the National Academy of Sciences, Washington, D. C.

The Board is not a government agency but receives its support from various private sources. At present it consists of 24 members who meet twice each year, and 15 committees, members of which are called Panel Members of the Food and Nutrition Board, who meet when necessary. The Board maintains liaison representation with the Food and Agriculture Organization of the United Nations, numerous government agencies, and with the various professional societies interested in nutrition. The total roster of the Board is over 50 persons, each of whom serves without recompense of any kind.

FIGURE 1

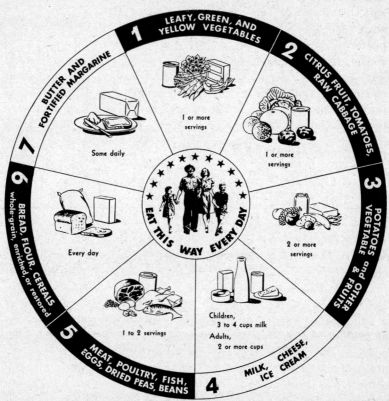

Courtesy U. S. Department of Agriculture

The chart of "The Basic Seven" was developed by the U. S. Department of Agriculture as a guide to proper food selection by consumers during World War II. The facts then emphasized serve equally well during peace-time as a guide to improved nutrition. Canned foods could be illustrated in almost all of the basic seven groups.

The Board has developed recommended dietary allowances, which were the subject of Chapter 2, as goals to be attained in the national dietary, and tables of food composition which help indicate how these allowances can be obtained. The Board has promoted the enrichment program for flour, bread and certain corn and rice products, and it has approved the fortification of margarine with vitamin A, and the iodization of table salt. The continued use of vitamin D milk on an expanded scale has been encouraged. The Board has initiated and supported the publication of a series of monographs dealing with foods and nutrition. A publication of interest to those engaged in nutrition research is a survey of such research in the United States (6). Another valuable publication is Bulletin 117 on "Nutrition Surveys: Their Techniques and Value" by a number of authors (7). These examples are cited to indicate in a small way the scope of the Board's interests in the field of nutrition.

The Council on Foods and Nutrition—A committee dealing with the problems of foods and nutritions, which has exerted great influence in guiding the food industry in the application of newer knowledge to food products, and the claims made for them, is the Council on Foods and Nutrition of the American Medical Association (8). This group was established as a small committee in 1929. It subsequently was expanded until in 1936 it was made a Council, or standing committee of the Board of Trustees of the American Medical Association, with a full-time secretary and staff, at the Chicago headquarters of the Association. Members of the Council serve without recompense. In the beginning the Council devoted most of its attention to health claims made for food products, and encouraged truthful labeling and advertising of products through a food product acceptance program. Later, after the Federal Food, Drug and Cosmetic Act of 1938 gave more rigid controls over food products and their labeling, and the Wheeler-Lea amendment gave expanded authority over advertising to the Federal Trade Commission, the Council restricted its scope of consideration of products to those of special medical interest, such as foods intended for the feeding of infants, special purpose foods for feeding the sick, and foods for which unusual health claims might be advanced. The Council has published in the Journal of the American Medical Association many monographs stating its opinion on the nutritional significance of classes of foods, or on matters of nutrition, and has served to keep the medical profession informed about newer developments in this field. In the past the Council helped guide the enrichment and fortification of foods with vitamins and minerals, and the retention of natural food factors during processing. At present the Council continues to exert its leadership in serving the medical profession and the public in matters that come within its purview, and it has encouraged the teaching of nutrition in the medical schools.

Other Organizations—Space does not permit discussion of the work of the American National Red Cross or of many other agencies concerned with the general problem of making prompt and effective use of nutritional knowledge for the benefit of the public. Even in the case of the organizations mentioned only a sketchy outline of their functions is possible, but it is hoped that enough has been given to show how their work fits into the picture of nutrition education as a whole. The home economists and the nutritionists of the country, the teachers of foods and nutrition in educational institutions from elementary schools to great universities, individually and collectively as professional organizations contribute greatly to the work. That the efforts of all these professional groups are effective no one will deny. Examination of the statistics on food consumption shows the national dietary to be changing, and for the better. Agriculture and the food processing industries are meeting the demand for a wiser selection of foods in order to secure maximum health benefits for the nation. The canning industry, like other major food industries, is cooperating wholeheartedly in this movement to make advantageous use of the newer and still growing knowledge of the relationship of foods to health and disease.

The Canadian Nutrition Program

Other countries are likewise becoming more nutrition conscious. The Canadian Nutrition Program in its existing well-organized form stems abruptly from the World War II emergency (9). The Canadian Council on Nutrition was formed in 1937, and it sponsored limited dietary surveys and some research under grants from the Federal Health Department. The real impetus to activity came after 1939.

In 1941, the Federal Division of Nutrition was organized as a unit of the Department of National Health and Welfare. The general objective has been to aid in the improvement of nutritional status. In one of their annual reports this broad program of activities is outlined in the following manner:

1. Research activities including dietary and nutrition surveys and tabulations.
2. Nutrition education by contacts with provisions. Most of the nutrition material now used in Canada is produced by the Federal Division. A special system has been developed of planning this material at an annual meeting with representatives of each province, followed by consultation at each succeeding step in production.
3. Advice on group feeding, or quantity food service which is being given on request to industries, camps, small hospitals, institutions, Indian residential schools, etc. A test kitchen is operated to help in this phase of the program.
4. Specific information on nutrition, such as to answer letters from the public, or to compile the Table of Food Values, is the work of a Reference Section.
5. Special relations carried out by the Director on behalf of the Department or other government agencies. Eight out of 10 provinces in Canada have nutritionists employed for this program, and the other two collaborate through public health nurses. There has been a strengthening of the program also through official conferences in F.A.O., and more directly, with nutrition groups in the United States.

During the war, special prominence was given to industrial nutrition, and at first the work of the Division of Nutrition

Services was largely along industrial lines. This agency applied its efforts to assisting the war industries through providing better food facilities for their employees. This work is now carried over to other fields of group feeding.

Emphasis has been placed also on research on nutritional status, with the aim of basing local educational procedures on improvement of the weak points in the dietary habits. Methods have been compared with those in use in the United States and in Great Britain. Dietary, biochemical, clinical, and therapeutic techniques are all employed. Over 4,000 children and 2,000 adults in different areas in Canada have been studied, and this specialized service is in steady demand. A large project with Sioux Indians has been started to test some of the suggested ways of improving the nutritional status of the Indians. As a guide to food selection for all persons there were developed a set of instructions known as Canada's Food Rules. These rules are similar in many respects to the Basic Seven food rules of the United States.

International Programs

Since the close of World War II the United Nations organization has undertaken an ambitious program to implement nutritional education on an international basis. The Food and Agricultural Organization (F.A.O.) of the United Nations maintains the only world-wide nutrition program functioning at the present time (10). F.A.O. came into being at Quebec, Canada, in October, 1945, where 42 nations signed its Constitution. Its creation was a sequel to the work started in 1943 at Hot Springs, Virginia, by the United Nations Conference on Food and Agriculture. The membership of F.A.O. had increased to 58 countries by the beginning of the fourth year.

The main purposes of F.A.O. are set forth in the Preamble of its Constitution. They are directed towards raising levels of nutrition and standards of living among the peoples of member countries, towards securing improvements in the efficiency of the production and distribution of all food and agricultural products, and towards bettering the condition of rural populations and thus contributing to an expanding world economy.

F.A.O. is directed by a Conference which meets at least once a year and at which each member Nation has the right of one vote. An elected Council of 18 members has executive power between Conference sessions. The work of the Organization is carried out by its Secretariat which, in addition to administration and information services, is divided into six technical divisions: Nutrition, Agriculture, Forestry, Fisheries, Economics, and Rural Welfare.

F.A.O. is chiefly an advisory and coordinating organization and does not have authority to buy or distribute food, fertilizer, farm machinery, or other supplies. A major part of its program is the provision of technical assistance to Member governments. This is done by the collection, coordination, and circulation of information on plans, programs, and scientific developments in Member countries. In addition, individual technical experts, and in some cases large missions, are sent on request to advise countries on special subjects.

The importance of national nutrition organizations, whose principal functions are to guide governments on nutrition policy and to participate in the planning of national food programs, has been stressed by the F.A.O. Conference and by the Standing Committee on Nutrition.

Research on food and nutrition is not undertaken directly nor supported by F.A.O. However, encouragement and advice are given on such subjects and on others, including diet surveys, nutrition education and school feeding.

The Nutrition Division of F.A.O. cooperates with the United Nations International Children's Emergency Fund, which began feeding programs for children and mothers in 12 European countries in 1945 and is now expanding its activities into the Far East and East Asia. It also cooperates with the Nutrition Division of the new World Health Organization

(W.H.O.). The latter organization deals with problems of medical nutrition, among others, and the nutrition work of both W.H.O. and F.A.O. are coordinated by meetings of representatives of both groups.

Objectives of Nutrition Education

The brief description in this Chapter of the agencies and methods involved in nutrition education will have served its purpose if it indicates the vast scope of the field of applied nutrition and nutrition education of the public. These activities make Nutrition the most practical of the sciences which daily affect the life and health of each individual person. In the opinion of many students of Nutrition, fear and strife between nations will largely be abolished when Hunger and Malnutrition have disappeared among their peoples. The science of Nutrition indicates how dietary deficiencies may be overcome. The problem is to put this knowledge to use, and that is the objective of all community, national and international programs on Nutrition.

REFERENCES

1. The Nutrition Foundation, Inc. *Report of Scientific Director.* New York, 1949.
2. Division of The Federal Register. *United States Government Manual* (Revised through June 30, 1948). The National Archives, Washington, D. C.
3. Bureau of Human Nutrition and Home Economics. *Report of the Chief of the Bureau of Human Nutrition and Home Economics, Agricultural Research Administration.* U. S. Government Printing Office, Washington, D. C., 1949.
4. *Report on Food and Nutrition Work of the Federal Agencies Represented on the Interdepartmental Nutrition Coordinating Committee, 1948; and other material compiled by the Nutrition Programs Office, Production and Marketing Administration,* U. S. Department of Agriculture, Washington, D. C.
5. Voris, L. *The Food and Nutrition Board of the National Research Council.* Nutritional Observatory 9, 43-48, 1948.
6. Food and Nutrition Board, National Research Council. *Survey of Food and Nutrition Research in the United States, 1947.* National Research Council, Washington, D. C., 1948.

7. Food and Nutrition Board, National Research Council. *Nutrition Surveys: Their Techniques and Value.* Bull. 117, Washington, D. C., 1949.

8. Fishbein, M. *A History of the American Medical Association 1847 to 1949.* W. B. Saunders Co., Philadelphia, 1947 (Wilson, J. R. The Council on Foods and Nutrition 936-947).

9. Pett, L. B. Canadian Nutrition Policy. *Nutrition for Young and Old.* New York State Joint Legislative Committee on Nutrition, 44-47, 1946. 94 Broadway, Newburgh New York.

10. Food and Agriculture Organization of the United Nations. *National Progress in Food and Agricultural Programs.* Washington, D. C., 1948.

Chapter 4

CANNED FOOD NUTRITION RESEARCH

A program of study of the nutritive value of canned foods has been pursued by the canning industry since 1922. At that time the foundations of nutrition had been established and a volume of literature had appeared describing the occurrence of known vitamins in foods and the stabilities of these factors under various conditions of treatment or handling. In some of this work canned foods had been specifically studied. In other reports the influence on vitamins in foods of heat and oxygen, such as might be involved during canning operations, had also been investigated.

A review of the data by Kohman, in a bulletin of the National Canners Association published in 1922 (1), indicated that, despite the presence of oxygen and heat treatments imposed during canning, canned foods retained significant amounts of the vitamins then known to be essential in human nutrition. In the following year, because of increased popular and scientific interest in the matter of vitamins in all classes of foods, it was considered essential that more information be adduced on the vitamin contents of commercially canned foods as well as on the influence of specific conditions or operations in canning procedures on vitamin retention. Consequently, a cooperative program between the National Canners Association and Teachers College, Columbia University, was arranged. These studies which were carried out by Eddy, Kohman, and their associates between 1923 and 1937, have been well described and summarized by Kohman (2). This cooperative project represents the longest sustained nutrition program ever devoted to any class of processed or packaged food up to the present time.

57

The initial publication resulting from this program, which covered the influence of variations in time and temperature of heating on vitamin C retention in cabbage (3) was followed by other papers (4-14). These publications related either to the vitamin potency of canned foods, or to the effect of canning on vitamins in foods such as apples, spinach, turnip greens, peas, peaches, strawberries, pears, grapefruit, prunes, and tomatoes and related products (tomato juice and paste).

The effects of storage were also investigated by Kohman and Eddy in a preliminary way. Other studies covered certain aspects of calcium and vitamin D in foods and animal maintenance on a total canned food diet. Reports also followed on the influence of canned foods on the changing American dietary; on the comparative effects on animals of canned, home cooked, and raw food diets; and on the antirachitic effect of some foods (15-19).

Most of the work of Eddy and Kohman was carried out during the period when bioassays requiring the use of experimental animals were employed for estimation of vitamin content or potency. Many of these early bioassay techniques measured the effects of vitamin factors which subsequently were resolved into several entities. Despite these limitations, the pioneer work of Kohman and Eddy established the basic principles of vitamin retention in canned foods which later work has served largely either to verify or to place upon more exact or quantitative bases.

Other Studies—Between 1930 and 1940 a number of reports of nutrition research on canned foods appeared. Due primarily to the interest in this subject stimulated by the studies of Kohman and Eddy, laboratories associated with can manufacturers, various Government Bureaus, Experiment Stations, and educational institutions undertook investigation of specific phases of nutrition research on canned foods. During this same period there was also increased interest in ascertaining the effect of home food preparatory or preserving operations on vitamins in common foods (20-23).

These advances in knowledge led to the preparation of a valuable series of bulletins listing the nutrient compositions of many raw and canned foods (24-27). A selected bibliography of the major papers covering vitamin research on canned foods since 1922 is to be found in a recent publication (28). The principal publications in this field since 1937 are also to be found in the Apppendix.

The National Canners Association—Can Manufacturers Institute Nutrition Program

During the National Nutrition Conference for Defense, called by the President in May, 1941, the need for more quantitative data on the nutritive value of canned foods became apparent. This need was discussed by executives of the National Canners Association; the cooperation of the Can Manufacturers Institute in a new nutrition program on canned foods was solicited and obtained; funds to support one year's study were assured; and a special committee was created to study the problem and recommend a plan of experimentation for the proposed program as well as a means for its administration. During the Summer and Fall of 1941, at the height of the national defense period, this committee explored the possibilities of inaugurating the new program. Agreement was quickly reached as to the possible experimental pattern of the program.

Several definite objectives were established for this program. Important practical objectives were:

1. To inventory the nutritional value of a variety of canned foods, and
2. To acquire information that would show the way to improvement in nutrient retentions where such improvements was indicated.

It was to be an industry project designed to provide scientific groups, dietitians, home economists, and others with usable dietary information, and the industry with technological facts on product improvement.

Administration—Administration of the program was finally designated as the responsibility of an Executive Committee of five scientists, including three representatives from the National Canners Association laboratories and two appointed to represent the Can Manufacturers Institute. This Committee has planned and arranged the execution of all projects sponsored under this program. In its work it has had the assistance of an Industry Advisory Committee and three regional committees, each of the latter being under the chairmanship of a member of the Executive Committee. This arrangement has greatly facilitated handling of local problems such as the collection of samples and contacts with collaborating institutions.

Pattern of the Nutrition Program—In considering the type and scope of the work to be undertaken in the first year of operation, it appeared that the work to be done logically fell into two distinct categories or phases, namely:

> 1. Determination of the specific influences or effects of commercial canning operations on the nutrients in raw canning stocks with the ultimate purpose of improving retention of such nutrients in the final product. This phase also includes other studies of a specialized type related to improvement of the nutritive values of canned foods.
>
> 2. Establishment of the nutritive values of foods canned by modern practices with respect to their contributions of vitamins, minerals, and the proximate food components such as carbohydrate, protein and fat.

These respective phases of the work were listed in the order in which they preferably would be undertaken under normal circumstances and under the most favorable conditions of time and personnel. However, as indicated, planning of the program was carried out in the periods shortly before and after Pearl Harbor and the urgent needs of agencies charged with proper nutrition of the armed forces required first consideration. There was a demand from these agencies for more exhaustive information on the composition of all types of foods, particularly with reference to vitamin values. So important was this need that in 1941 the National Research Council appointed a Food Composition Committee to compile and tabulate information on the subject from all possible sources and especially data previously unreported by industry (29). Therefore, in deference to the current and pressing needs, in the first year emphasis was placed on the establishment of the nutritive values of canned foods as then manufactured. This type of activity was designated as "Phase I". After examining the results of the first year's work, both sponsoring bodies approved continuation of the program. It then became possible during the second year to begin so-called "Phase II" studies, namely, the determination by modern methods and techniques of the specific effects of canning operations and other commercial and consumer practices on nutrients in raw foods and the study of ways and means of increasing retentions of these essential factors. The N.C.A.-C.M.I. program in 1950 reached its eighth year and Phase II activities then constituted the major portion of the projects under way.

Execution of Projects—In the initial planning, the guiding policy was laid down that, in so far as possible, actual experimentation should lie in the hands of competent investigators in educational institutions well known for their work in the field of nutrition. The first task of the Executive Committee was therefore to allocate the work on hand to various institutions through research grants, or grants-in-aid. Fortunately, the type of work involved in the program as well as the objectives of the program itself proved attractive to a number of outstanding colleges and universities and their collaboration was readily secured.

Following is a list of the universities at which the nutrition work was done and the number of grants placed with each university:

Location and Number of Nutrition Grants

Location	*Number of Grants*
Cornell University (New York Agricultural Experiment Station)	2
Michigan Agricultural Experiment Station	2
Pennsylvania State College	5
University of Arizona	1
University of California, at Los Angeles	1
University of Chicago	4
University of Maryland	4
University of Texas	1
University of Wisconsin	7
Total	27

The information thus developed has provided a broad insight into the nutritional value of canned foods, yielding information applicable to the needs of food specialists, home economics experts, the armed forces, and those interested in institutional feeding.

The program thus far has received financial support of more than $250,000. This is not a measure of the total cost, however, since a considerable part of the project involved specialized responsibility which could only be assumed by laboratories connected with the canning industry. Consequently, it was necessary for the research divisions of the American Can Company, the Continental Can Company, Inc., and the San Francisco, Seattle, and Washington laboratories of the National Canners Association to engage in such activities quite apart from the institutional collaborative studies to which reference has been made.

Sampling Procedure

The initial studies in the N.C.A.-C.M.I. canned foods nutrition program involved the collection and analysis of approximately 900 samples of commercially canned foods (30). More than 30 different products were included in the survey, and more were added later. The products studied initially included canned fruits, vegetables, and fish or marine products. The canned fruits were: Apricots, grapefruit (segments and juice), orange juice, peaches, pears, purple plums (prunes), and pineapple (sliced and juice). The canned vegetables were: Asparagus (green and white), baked beans, green and Lima beans, beets, carrots, whole grain corn (white and yellow), peas (sweet* and Alaska), spinach, tomatoes, and tomato juice. The canned fish and marine products were: Mackerel, salmon, sardines (oil and sauce styles), shrimp (wet and dry pack), and tuna. The limitations in the number of products examined permitted a comprehensive study of each product, while at the same time the number of products examined was sufficient to afford a broad, general picture of the nutritional value of canned foods as a group.

Members of the canning industry gave their wholehearted cooperation to the program from the beginning. In the case of each product steps were taken to assure the inclusion in the samples analyzed of products from the various major areas of production (31). As illustrative of the efforts which were taken to obtain samples that would be representative of the entire pack of each product, Figures 2 to 6 are provided. These Figures show the areas where samples of a few of the products were obtained, namely, canned peas, tomato juice, orange juice, tomatoes, pineapple and pineapple juice, salmon, shrimp, and tuna.

Samples of each canned food were collected at the canneries by representatives of the industry who were designated for this purpose. A sampling as a rule represented a day's pack of a product in one can size. Early, mid, and late-season samplings were usually obtained from each cannery. The history of each sample was recorded, information being taken about the raw products used and the canning procedures

---

* This term is commonly applied in the canning industry to wrinkled varieties of peas as contrast to the smooth varieties of Alaska peas.

FIGURE 2

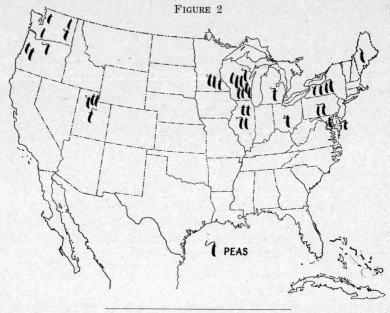

PEAS

FIGURE 3

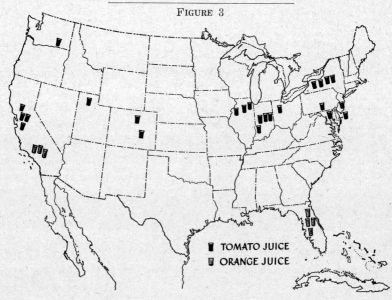

■ TOMATO JUICE
▯ ORANGE JUICE

FIGURE 4

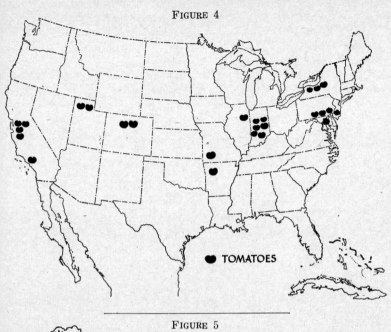

● TOMATOES

FIGURE 5

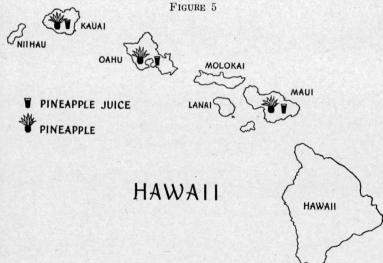

KAUAI

NIIHAU

OAHU

MOLOKAI

MAUI

LANAI

▮ PINEAPPLE JUICE

🍍 PINEAPPLE

HAWAII

HAWAII

FIGURE 6

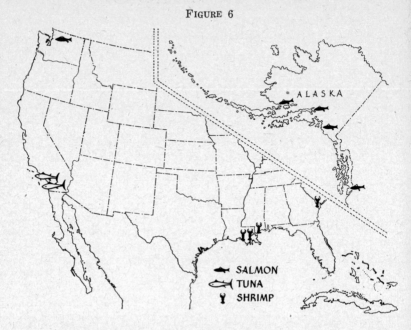

employed, with the thought that a study of these data later might reveal trends in the results which would be of possible value in later studies of nutrient retention (32).

Both retail size cans, as used by homemakers, and larger institutional size cans were collected. These samples were marked for identification, sent to a central collection station for inspection and coding, and then sent to the different collaborators who participated in the program for examination.

Summary of Results

In subsequent Chapters specific findings resulting from the N.C.A.-C.M.I. program are presented in discussions of the nutritive values of commercially canned foods as disclosed in the Phase I investigations. Briefly it may be stated that foods canned commercially by modern methods retain in substantial degree all nutrients characteristic of the respective raw foods. Certain investigations which were conducted showed that while retentions of nutrients in many instances are quite satisfactory, there is evidence that modifications in certain canning operations as well as some changes in consumer preparatory and commercial storage practices would improve nutrient retention of canned foods. For convenience, the complete list of these publications is reproduced at the end of this Chapter.

Future Planning—Referring to the N.C.A.-C.M.I. nutrition program, a recent publication has stated (33) :

> "In 1942 a large-scale survey of the nutritive value of canned foods was begun under the joint sponsorship of the National Canners Association and the Can Manufacturers Institute. At the end of the first year progress reports were issued from the laboratories which were cooperating in the survey.
>
> "Since that time approximately two dozen papers have appeared, dealing with the contents of several 'B vitamins,' fat-soluble vitamins, and minerals in canned foods, the reproducibility of assay values, and the effect of processing, storage, etc., on nutritive value.
>
> "In general it may be said that canned foods retain a large part of the original nutritive values of the foods. The distribution of nutrients between solid and liquid portions of canned foods varies widely. Both solid and liquid portions have good nutritive values.
>
> "The over-all program of the National Canners Association and the Can Manufacturers Institute, which has been carried through by the various cooperating laboratories, has resulted in a better understanding of the contributions made by canned foods to national nutrition, and it may be said that more is known about the nutritive values of canned foods than about any other type of processed food."

During the past five years chief emphasis has been placed on the Phase II work in the belief that disclosures made in such work when applied in commercial practices should raise the general nutritive levels of commercially canned foods. Future activities in the program will aim to provide to the fullest possible extent information on the nutritive values of canned foods and to encourage every reasonable or practicable improvement in operations so as to insure the highest nutritive level in canned foods.

N.C.A.-C.M.I. NUTRITION PUBLICATIONS

The major publications emanating from the N.C.A.-C.M.I. nutrition program to date of publication under the title "The Nutritive Value of Canned Foods" are as follows:

I. Clifcorn, L. E. *Introduction and Sampling Procedure.* J. Nutrition 28, 101-105, 1944.

II. Pressley, A., Ridder, C., Smith, M. C. and Caldwell, E. *Ascorbic Acid and Carotene or Vitamin A Content.* J. Nutrition 28, 107-116, 1944.

III. Ives, M., Wagner, J. R., Elvehjem, C. A. and Strong, F. M. *Thiamine and Niacin.* J. Nutrition 28, 117-121, 1944.

IV. Thompson, M. L., Cunningham, E. and Snell, E. E. *Riboflavin and Pantothenic Acid.* J. Nutrition 28, 123-129, 1944.

V. Brush, M. K., Hinman, W. F. and Halliday, E. G. *Distribution of Water Soluble Vitamins Between Solid and Liquid Portions of Canned Vegetables and Fruits.* J. Nutrition 28, 131-140, 1944.

VI. Hinman, W. F., Brush, M. K. and Halliday, E. G. *Effect of Large-Scale Preparation for Serving on the Ascorbic Acid, Thiamin, and Riboflavin Content of Commercially-Canned Vegetables.* J. Am Dietet. Assoc. 20, 752-756, 1944.

VII. Hinman, W. F., Brush, M. K. and Halliday, E. G. *Effect of Small-Scale Preparation for Serving on the Ascorbic Acid, Thiamin, and Riboflavin Content of Commercially-Canned Vegetables.* J. Am. Dietet. Assoc. 21, 7-10, 1945.

VIII. Kramer, A. *Distribution of Proximate and Mineral Nutrients in the Drained and Liquid Portions of Canned Vegetables.* J. Am. Dietet. Assoc. 21, 354-356, 1945.

IX. Wagner, J. R., Ives, M., Strong, F. M. and Elvehjem, C. A. *Effect of Commercial Canning and Short-Time Storage on Ascorbic Acid Content of Grapefruit Juice.* Food Research 10, 469-475, 1945.

X. Ives, M., Zepplin, M., Ames, S. R., Strong, F. M. and Elvehjem, C. A. *Further Studies on Riboflavin, Niacin, and Pantothenic Acid.* J. Am. Dietet. Assoc. 21, 357-359, 1945.

XI. Guerrant N. B., Vavich, M. G., and Fardig, O. B. *Comparison of Vitamin Values Obtained by Different Methods of Assay.* Ind. Eng. Chem., Anal. Ed. 17, 710-713, 1945.

XII. Vavich, M. G., Stern, R. M. and Guerrant, N. B. *Determination of Ascorbic Acid of Fresh Green Peas.* Ind. Eng. Chem., Anal. Ed. 17, 531, 1945.

XIII. Guerrant, N. B., Vavich, M. G. and Dutcher, R. A. *Influence of Temperature and Time of Storage on Vitamin Contents.* Ind. Eng. Chem. 37, 1240-1243, 1945.

XIV. Wagner, J. R. Strong, F. M. and Elvehjem, C. A. *Effect of Commercial Canning Operations on the Ascorbic Acid, Thiamine, Riboflavin, and Niacin Contents of Vegetables.* Ind. Eng. Chem. 39, 985-990, 1947.

XV. Wagner, J. R., Strong, F. M. and Elvehjem, C. A. *Effects of Blanching on the Retention of Ascorbic Acid, Thiamine, and Niacin in Vegetables.* Ind. Eng. Chem. 39, 990-993, 1947.

XVI. Kramer, A. *Proximate and Mineral Composition.* Food Research 11, 391-398, 1946.

XVII. Ives, M., Pollard, A. E., Elvehjem, C. A. and Strong, F. M. *Pyridoxine, Biotin, and "Folic Acid".* J. Nutrition 31, 347-353, 1946.

XVIII. Hinman, W. F., Higgins, M. M. and Halliday, E. G. *Further Studies on Carotene, Ascorbic Acid, and Thiamine.* J. Am. Dietet. Assoc. 23, 226-231, 1947.

XIX. Lamb, F. C. *Factors Affecting Ascorbic Acid Content of Canned Grapefruit and Orange Juices.* Ind. Eng. Chem. 38, 860-864, 1946.

XX. Guerrant, N. B., Vavich, M. G., Fardig, O. B., Dutcher, R. A. and Stern, R. M. *Changes in the Vitamin Content of Foods During Canning.* J. Nutrition 32, 435-458, 1946.

XXI. Lamb, F. C., Pressley, A. and Zuch, T. *Retention of Nutrients During Commercial Production of Various Canned Fruits and Vegetables.* Food Research 12, 273-287, 1947.

XXII. Moschette, D. S., Hinman, W. F. and Halliday, E. G. *Effect of Time and Temperature of Storage on Vitamin Content of Commercially Canned Fruits and Fruit Juices. (Stored 12 Months).* Ind. Eng. Chem. 39, 994-999, 1947.

XXIII. Guerrant, N. B., Vavich, M. G., Fardig, O. B., Ellenberger, H. A., Stern, R. M. and Coonen, N. H. *Effect of Duration and Temperature of Blanch on Vitamin Retention by Certain Vegetables.* Ind. Eng. Chem. 39, 1000-1007, 1947.

XXIV. Kramer, A. and Smith, M. H. *Effect of Duration and Temperature of Blanch on Proximate and Mineral Composition of Certain Vegetables.* Ind. Eng. Chem. 39, 1007-1009, 1947.

XXV. Neilands, J. B., Strong, F. M. and Elvehjem, C. A. *Vitamin Content of Canned Fish Products.* J. Nutrition 34, 633-643, 1947.

XXVI. Sheft, B. B., Griswold, R. M., Tarlowsky, E. and Halliday, E. G. *Effect of Time and Temperature of Storage on Vitamin Content of Commercially Canned Fruits and Fruit Juices (Stored 18 and 24 Months).* Ind. Eng. Chem. 41, 144-145, 1949.

XXVII. Guerrant, N. B., Fardig, O. B., Vavich, M. G., and Ellenberger, H. A. *Influence of Temperature and Time of Storage on Vitamin Content.* Ind. Eng. Chem. **40**, 2258-2263, 1948.

XXVIII. Monroe, K. H., Brighton, K. W. and Bendix, G. H. *Some Studies of Commercial Warehouse Temperatures With Reference to the Stability of Vitamins in Canned Foods.* Food Technology **3**, 292-299, 1949.

XXIX. Heberlein, D. G., Ptak, L. R., Medoff, S. and Clifcorn, L. E. *Quality and Nutritive Value of Peas as Affected by Blanching.* Food Technology **4**, 104-114, 1950.

XXX. Marshall, R. E. and Robertson, W. F. *I. Handling and Storage Procedures for Vegetables Prior to Canning.* Food Technology **2**, 133-143, 1948.

XXXI. Feaster, J. F., Mudra, A. E., Ives, M. and Tompkins, M. D. *Effect of Blanching Time on Vitamin Retention in Canned Peas.* The Canner **108**, No. 1, 27-30, 1949.

XXXII. Paul, P., Einbecker, B. Kelley, L. Jackson, M. Jackson, L., Marshall, R. E., Robertson, W. F. and Ohlson, M. A. *II. Changes in Ascorbic Acid of Vegetables During Storage Prior to Canning.* Food Technology **3**, 228-231, 1949.

XXXIII. Dunn, M. S., Camien, M. N., Eiduson, S. and Malin, R. B. *I. Amino Acid Content of Fish and Meat Products.* J. Nutrition **39**, 177-185, 1949.

XXXIII. Neilands, J. B., Sirny, R. J., Sohljell, I., Strong, F. M. and Elvehjem, C. A. *II. Amino Acid Content of Fish and Meat Products.* J. Nutrition **39**, 187-202, 1949.

XXXV. Lamb, F. C., Lewis, L. D. and Lee, S. K. *Effect of Blanching on Retention of Ascorbic Acid and Thiamine in Peas.* Western Canner and Packer **40**, 6, 60-62, 1948.

XXXVIII. Ingalls, R., Brewer, W. D., Tobey, H. L., Plummer J., Bennett, B. B. and Ohlson, M. A. *III. Changes in Riboflavin Content of Vegetables During Storage Prior to Canning.* Food Technology **4**, 258-263, 1950.

XXXIX. Robinson, W. B., Moyer, J. C. and Kertesz, Z. I. *"Thermal Maceration" of Plant Tissue.* Plant Physiology **24**, 317-319, 1949.

XL. Ingalls, R., Brewer, W. D., Tobey, H. L., Plummer, J., Bennett, B. B. and Paul, P. *IV. Changes in Thiamine Content of Vegetables During Storage Prior to Canning.* Food Technology **4**, 264-268, 1950.

XLI. Kelley, L., Bennett, B. B. Rafferty, J. P. and Paul, P. *V. Changes in Carotene Content of Vegetables During Storage Prior to Canning.* Food Technology **4**, 269-272, 1950.

REFERENCES
1. Kohman, E. F. *Vitamins in Canned Foods.* Bull. 19-L, National Canners Assoc., Washington, D.C. 1922.
2. Kohman, E. F. *Vitamins in Canned Foods.* Bull. 19-L, 4th Rev. National Canners Assoc., Washington, D.C. 1937.
3. Eddy, W. H. and Kohman, E. F. *Vitamin C in Canned Foods.* Ind. Eng. Chem. 16, 52-53, 1924.
4. Kohman, E. F., Eddy, W. H. and Carlsson, V. *Vitamins in Canned Foods. II. The Vitamin C Destructive Factor in Apples.* Ind. Eng. Chem. 16, 1261-1263, 1924.
5. Eddy, W. H., Kohman, E. F. and Carlsson, V. *Vitamins in Canned Foods. III. Canned Spinach.* Ind. Eng. Chem. 17, 69-74, 1925.
6. Eddy, W. H., Kohman, E. F. and Carlsson, V. *Vitamins in Canned Foods. IV. Green Peas.* Ind. Eng. Chem. 18, 85-89, 1926.
7. Kohman, E. F., Eddy, W. H., Carlsson, V. and Halliday, N. *Vitamins in Canned Foods. V. Peaches.* Ind. Eng. Chem. 18, 302-303, 1926.
8. Kohman, E. F., Eddy, W. H. and Halliday, N. *Vitamins in Canned Foods. VI. Strawberries.* Ind. Eng. Chem. 20, 202-204, 1928.
9. Eddy, W. H., Kohman, E. F. and Halliday, N. *Vitamins in Canned Foods. VII. Effect of Storage on Vitamin Value of Canned Spinach.* Ind. Eng. Chem. 21, 347, 1929.
10. Kramer, M. M., Eddy, W. H. and Kohman, E. F. *Vitamins in Canned Foods. VIII. Home Canning and Commercial Canning Contrasted in Their Effects on Vitamin Values of Pears.* Ind. Eng. Chem. 21, 859-861, 1929.
11. Kohman, E. F., Eddy, W. H. and Zall, C. *Vitamins in Canned Foods. IX. Tomato Products.* Ind. Eng. Chem. 22, 1015-1017, 1930.
12. Kohman, E. F., Eddy, W. H. and Gurin, C. Z. *Vitamins in Canned Foods. X. The Vitamin Content of Some Canned Vegetables.* Ind. Eng. Chem. 23, 808-811, 1931.
13. Eddy, W. H., Gurin, C. Z. and Kohman, E. F. *Vitamins in Canned Foods. XII. Supplementary Nature of Grapefruit and Prunes.* Ind. Eng. Chem. 24, 457-460, 1932.
14. Kohman, E. F., Eddy, W. H. and Gurin, C. Z. *Vitamins in Canned Foods. XIII. Canning Tomato Juice Without Vitamin C Loss.* Ind. Eng. Chem. 25, 682-684, 1933.
15. Kohman, E. F., Eddy, W. H. and Gurin, C. Z. *Vitamins in Canned Foods. XI. A Canned Food Diet.* Ind. Eng. Chem. 23, 1064-1066, 1931.
16. Kohman, E. F. *Stabilizing Nutrients by Canning.* Ind. Eng. Chem. 24, 650-654, 1932.
17. Kohman, E. F., Sanborn, N. H., Eddy, W. H. and Gurin, C. Z. *Vitamins in Canned Foods. XIV. Calcium and Vitamin D in Foods.* Ind. Eng. Chem. 26, 758-761, 1934.
18. Kohman, E. F., Eddy, W. H., White, M. E. and Sanborn, N. H. *Comparative Experiments with Canned, Home Cooked and Raw Food Diets.* J. Nutrition, 14, 9-19, 1937.

19. Kohman, E. F., Eddy, W. H., White, M. E. and Sanborn, N. H. *The Antirachitic Effect of Some Foods.* Food Research **3**, 373-381, 1938.

20. Aughey, E. and Daniel, E. P. *Effect of Cooking Upon the Thiamine Content of Foods.* J. Nutrition, **19**, 285-296, 1940.

21. Daniel, E. P. and Rutherford, M. B. *Effect of Home Canning and Storage. Ascorbic Acid Content of Tomatoes.* Food Research **1**, 341-347, 1936.

22. Fenton, F. and Tressler, D. K. *Losses of Vitamin C During the Cooking of Certain Vegetables.* J. Home Econ. **30**, 717-722, 1938.

23. Lantz, E. M. *The Riboflavin and Vitamin B6 Content of Pinto Beans and the Effect of Cooking on These Factors.* J. Home Econ. **32**, 107-112, 1940.

24. Booher, L. E., Hartzler, E. R. and Hewston, E. M. *A Compilation of the Vitamin Values of Foods in Relation to Processing and Other Variants.* U. S. Dept. Agr. Cir. **638**, 1942.

25. Adams, G. and Smith, S. L. *Experiment Station Research on the Vitamin Content and the Preservation of Foods.* U. S. Dept. Agr. Misc. Publ. **536**, 1944.

26. Chatfield, C. and Adams, G. *Proximate Composition of American Food Materials.* U. S. Dept. Agr. Circ. **549**, 1940.

27. *Tables of Food Composition in Terms of Eleven Nutrients.* U. S. Dept. Agr. Misc. Publ. **572**, 1945.

28. *The Canned Food Reference Manual. 3rd Ed.* American Can Co., New York, 1947.

29. Pavcek, P. L. and Elvehjem, C. A. *Work of the Committee on Food Composition.* J. Amer. Dietet. Assoc. **20**, 216-219, 1944.

30. Pilcher R. W. *The First Year's Findings in the NCA-CMI Nutrition Program.* National Canners Association, Supplement to Information Letter, No. 1034, April 28, 1945.

31. Nutrition Research Executive Committee, National Canners Association. Studies on The Nutritive Value of Canned Goods. Executive Committee Progress Report No. 1, December 31, 1942.

32. Clifcorn, L. E. *The Nutritive Value of Canned Foods. I. Introduction and Sampling Procedure.* J. Nutrition, **28**, 101-105, 1944.

33. *Current Research in the Science of Nutrition as Reviewed in the May Issue of Nutrition Reviews.* Nutrition Foundation, Inc., New York, 1949.

Section II

NUTRITIVE VALUES OF CANNED FOODS

THE GENERAL COMPOSITION OF CANNED FOODS

In the analysis of foods to obtain data regarding their composition in terms of constituents of nutritional interest it has long been customary to make determinations of the so-called proximate principles. There are thus obtained figures for the protein, fat, carbohydrate, ash and moisture content of the foods. From these data the caloric value of the foods may be calculated, by using the appropriate factors for conversion. These are standard practices in the laboratory examination of foods.

The moisture content is determined as a rule by heating a sample of the food under appropriate conditions and determining the loss of weight. (The percentage of total solids may be obtained by subtracting the percentage of moisture from 100.) The protein is estimated by determination of the total nitrogen content and multiplying this value by 6.25. This factor is used because the average nitrogen content of proteins is 16 per cent. The fat content is estimated by measurement of the amount of material extractable by ether. Ash is measured by determination of the weight of the residue after incineration. The sum of these values, when subtracted from 100 gives a value which is called total carbohydrate.

The data of ordinary food analyses are at best approximate. There are other substances in foods which do not show up in the general analysis of the food, for example, the vitamins, which are present in small amounts. The conventional method of estimating protein content by measuring nitrogen and multiplying by a factor does not preclude the possibility of non-protein nitrogen components being recorded as protein. As a rule, however, such non-protein nitrogen compounds are present in but small amounts in foods, and some of the material may be in the form of amino acids or peptides which would be nutritionally considered as proteins. The determination of fat content by measuring the amount of substances extracted by ether does not exclude the extraction of ether-soluble materials other than true fat. Here again the amounts of such non-fat materials are small, and usually no serious error is introduced.

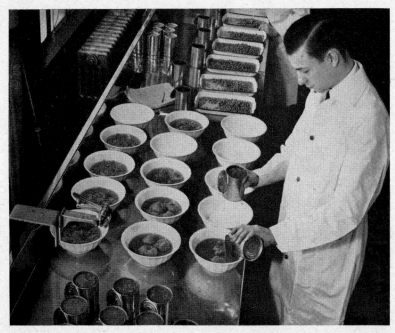

Courtesy Continental Can Company, Inc.

All canners are zealous in maintaining the quality of their brands. Shown in the illustration is the inspection of canned tomatoes and canned peas for appearance and eating quality.

Despite limitations, data on the general composition of foods can serve many useful purposes. Table I of the Appendix provides information about the proximate analysis of over 200 commercial canned food items. The data have been compiled from a number of reliable sources, as indicated in the foreword to the tables, and from the results of the canned food nutrition project. The Table is unique in that not only is the average value stated, but also the minimum and maximum values, together with the number of analyses. Each food product is carefully characterized as far as information available would permit. The data show the values for total solids, ash, fat, protein, crude fiber, carbohydrates other than crude fiber, and calories per 100 grams and per pound of food.

The present chapter will be concerned with a general discussion of the data about the proximate food components of canned foods, carbohydrates, fats, and calories. Discussion of the protein content of canned foods is deferred to another chapter.

The Carbohydrates of Foods

The carbohydrates are chiefly to be found in plant foods, in which they are formed by a process of photosynthesis. In this process, the carbon dioxide of the air is combined with water by a complicated series of reactions under the influence of sunlight, within plant cells which contain the green pigment, chlorophyll, to form starches and other carbohydrates. The carbohydrates contain carbon, hydrogen, and oxygen. Broadly speaking there are only a few forms of carbohydrates which must be considered from the viewpoint of nutrition. These are the monosaccharides, the disaccharides, and the polysaccharides.

The monosaccharides include the so-called "simple sugars" such as D-glucose, also known as grape sugar or dextrose, and frutose, sometimes called fruit sugar or levulose.

The best known of the disaccharides are sucrose, to which the sweetness of beets and sugar cane is due, lactose or milk sugar, and maltose or malt sugar, formed by germinating cereals and found in malt and malt products. Upon hydrolysis, either by acids or certain enzymes of the intestinal tract, the disaccharides break down to monosaccharides, one molecule of a disaccharide forming two molecules of mono-saccharides.

The polysaccharides are complex forms of carbohydrate found both in plants and animals. The most important is starch, which is present in many foods, particularly vegetables such as potatoes, cereal grains, and mature seeds of plants. Starch is digested in the alimentary tract to form D-glucose, in which form it is absorbed into the blood stream. Glycogen, or animal starch, is the animal counterpart of starch. It is contained in many animal tissues used as food, being present in largest amounts in fresh liver.

Mention should also be made of the polysaccharides known as dextrins. These are formed by the action of heat, acids or enzymes on starch. They are intermediate in complexity between starch and the disaccharides. They make up an appreciable part of the carbohydrates of corn syrup.

Crude-fiber—Another group of carbohydrate compounds sometimes designated as the "indigestible carbohydrates" also occurs in plant foods. These materials are chiefly the celluloses and hemicelluloses which form the framework of plant structures. After ingestion in foods, these materials resist digestion and are excreted. They thus provide bulk which is necessary for the normal muscular action of the intestine.

Collectively the indigestible carbohydrates are measured approximately by the determination of "fiber" or "crude fiber." The method includes treatment of the food sample with acid and with alkaline solutions, by which the digestible carbohydrates are thus removed. The residue is dried, extracted with ether, incinerated, and the loss of weight during ashing is taken as the weight of crude fiber. With meat products some of the cartilage may contribute to the material measured as crude fiber.

Determination of individual carbohydrates—Methods have been developed for the quantitative estimation of many of the individual carbohydrates, but these are seldom applied

to the analysis of foods for ordinary purposes. Some attention
has been given to the application of special methods of analysis, but usually for special purposes.

The Fats

The fats or lipids are also widely distributed in foods,
although the richest sources are foods of animal origin, such
as meats, meat and poultry products, certain species of fish,
and milk and other dairy products. Edible vegetable oils of
course are concentrated forms of fat.

The true fats are compounds formed from fatty acids and
glycerol into which components fats are split by the action
of intestinal juices. The fats are absorbed as such or after
hydrolysis under the influence of intestinal juices, followed
by resynthesis into fat before the material gets into the blood.

It has been mentioned previously that there are certain
unsaturated fatty acids which are essential, for the laboratory
rat. The function of the unsaturated essential fatty acids in
human nutrition still remains to be clarified. Presumably a
mixed diet of ordinary foods supplies sufficient unsaturated
fatty acids to meet any human requirement. Fats are important not only for their content of essential unsaturated fatty
acids, but also because they are a concentrated source of food
energy, their consumption gives rise to a feeling of satiety,
and in many of the natural food sources fats serve as carriers
of the fat-soluble vitamins. Fats are useful in helping to
bring out the flavor of many vegetables when prepared for
the table.

Calories

As has been stated, foods are broken down in the intestinal
tract by a series of hydrolytic changes under the influence of
enzymes of the gastro-intestinal juices. The carbohydrates
yield simple monosaccharides, and the proteins yield amino
acids, which are absorbed into the blood stream and transported to the liver and other organs and tissues of the body.

The fats are digested to fatty acids and glycerol, absorbed according to several possible routes, and reappear as fats in the blood. They likewise are transported to the liver and other body organs and tissues (1).

In the cells of the body the absorbed materials are converted into new materials for the maintenance of the body, or used directly in the production of material for new tissues, or they are oxidized to yield carbon dioxide, water and urea. Enzymes are important in cellular oxidations which effect these changes and, as will be indicated in later chapters, many of the vitamins function as components of the enzymes which are concerned with the oxidations within the cells.

The oxidation of products obtained in the digestion and absorption of carbohydrates, fats and proteins, results in the liberation of energy. This energy is used for body processes and physical work and eventually appears as heat. The over-all process can be measured in terms of heat units, or calories. Each gram of carbohydrate or protein is considered to result in the production of 4 calories, and each gram of fat, 9 calories, when digested, absorbed and oxidized by the body. American tables of food composition usually make use of these factors for computing the caloric values of foods.

Somewhat higher factors are obtained when foods are burned in a calorimeter and the production of heat is measured directly, even when allowance is made for the fact that proteins are not oxidized completely in the body, their nitrogen being excreted in the form of urea. The lower factors customarily employed, take into consideration the digestibility of foods, which is not quite complete. The 4, 4, and 9 factors for carbohydrate, protein, and fat, respectively, have been used in Table I of the Appendix.

Beginning with the classical tables of food composition of Atwater and Bryant in 1906 (2), a number of compilations of food composition have been made available (3-7). The information contained in tables published prior to the start of the canned food nutrition program, on canned foods produced and consumed in greatest annual volume, is relatively meager. To supply more adequate information on this subject provision was made in the canned food nutrition program for the determination of the proximate composition of more than 40 important commercially canned foods (8). Many additional data on the proximate composition of canned foods are also included in Table I of the Appendix.

The results on carbohydrate, fat and calories are discussed in the present Chapter. Protein and mineral determinations will be discussed in subsequent Chapters.

The Carbohydrate Content of Canned Foods

The raw foods from which canned foods are prepared show some variation in composition, which is reflected in the composition of the canned products. In the manufacture of certain canned vegetables, liquid is added to the can. This liquid, which may contain salt, sugar, or both, is usually added in amounts just sufficient to cover the product. In certain vegetable products, notably the "vacuum packed" vegetables, only a few ounces of this liquid are added to the product in the can. Therefore, from the standpoint of moisture or water content, the composition of canned and home cooked foods may for practical purposes be considered almost identical.

This may not be true with respect to the carbohydrate content. Canned food products packed in a liquid containing sugar will show correspondingly higher carbohydrate contents than their home cooked or prepared counterparts.

In work sponsored by the canned food nutrition program, Kramer (8) has reported the carbohydrate content of many canned foods. He also has suggested a convenient method of classifying canned foods according to their approximate carbohydrate content. This classification, which may prove useful in the management of both normal or restricted diets, is shown in Table 4. The values given are based upon the analysis of the entire contents of the can, including both the solid and liquid portions. This classification is somewhat more detailed than the so-called "5, 10, and 20 per cent" vegetable classification commonly used in calculation of diabetic and reducing dietary regimés (9).

TABLE 4

Carbohydrate Classification of Canned Foods

Adapted from: Kramer (8)

Approximate Carbohydrate Content	Canned Foods	
Per Cent		
25	Peaches, freestone Pineapple, sliced	Sweetpotatoes
22	Apricots Blackberries Corn, yellow, cream style	Peaches, cling Plums, purple (prunes)
19	Beans, baked Corn, white, cream style Corn, yellow, whole grain	Grapefruit segments Pears
14	Corn, white, whole grain	Pineapple juice
12	Beans, Lima, green Blueberries Cherries, red, sour, pitted	Grapefruit juice Orange juice Peas, Alaska
9	Beets Carrots	Peas, sweet Peppers
4	Asparagus, white Beans, green, cut Kraut	Pimientos Tomato juice Tomatoes
2	Asparagus, green Mushrooms Sardines, in tomato sauce	Spinach Turnip greens
1 or less	Mackerel Salmon Sardines, in oil	Shrimp Tuna

The average carbohydrate contents of canned foods on a serving basis are shown in Table X of the Appendix.

Fat Composition of Canned Foods

Fat is unaffected by canning procedures. Those foods which in the uncooked condition are low in fat are also low in fat after canning. A few products, such as sardines, may be packed in oil for canning, and the fat content of these products is increased. Available data on the fat content of many canned foods are provided in Table I of the Appendix; the average values of many canned foods on a serving basis are also provided in Table X.

Distribution of Soluble Proximate Principles

In the work of Kramer (10), a further study was made of the distribution of water-soluble nutrients between the solid and liquid phases in certain of the canned foods tested. As a general rule about one-third of the total water-soluble nutrients was found to be present in the the liquid portion.

Uses of Food Tables on Proximate Components of Foods

Food tables showing the composition of foods in terms of the proximate nutrients permit the selection of foods on a rational basis for many purposes. Not only can the nutritive value of diets be computed in terms of the total average probable composition in terms of the proximate constituents, but it is also possible to select foods that will make up a diet meeting various requirements, such as diets containing known amounts of protein, fat, carbohydrate, crude fiber, or calories. The use of tables of food composition is indispensable in the formulation of diets for diabetics, low residue diets, low fat diets, high or low caloric diets, and the like. The tables of food composition should make the task of formulation of therapeutic diets, containing canned foods, more convenient for the physician and dietitian.

REFERENCES

1. Council on Foods and Nutrition, American Medical Association. *Handbook of Nutrition.* Am. Med. Assoc., Chicago, 1943.
2. Atwater, W. O. and Bryant, A. P. *The Chemical Composition of American Food Materials.* U. S. Off. Expt. Sta. Bull. 28, 1906.
3. Chatfield, C. and Adams, G. *Proximate Composition of American Food Materials.* U. S. Dept. Agr. Circ. 549, 1940.
4. Bridges, M. A. *Dietetics for the Clinician. 4th Ed.* Lea and Febiger, Philadelphia, 1941.

5. Winton, A. L. and Winton, K. B. *The Structure and Composition of Foods. Vol. I, Cereals, Starch, Oil Seeds, Nuts, Oils, Forage Plants, 1932; Vol. II, Vegetables, Legumes, Fruits, 1935; Vol. III, Milk, Butter, Cheese, Ice Cream, Eggs, Meat, Meat Extracts, Gelatin, Animal Fats, Poultry, Fish, Shellfish, 1937; Vol. IV, Sugar, Sirup, Honey, Tea, Coffee, Cocoa, Spices, Extracts, Yeast, Baking Powder, 1939.* John Wiley & Sons, New York.

6. Sherman, H. C. *Chemistry of Food and Nutrition.* 7th Ed., Macmillan Co., New York, 1946.

7. *Tables of Food Composition in Terms of Eleven Nutrients,* U. S. Dept. Agr. Misc. Publ. 572, 1945.

8. Kramer, A. *Nutritive Value of Canned Foods. XVI. Proximate and Mineral Composition.* Food Research 11, 391-398, 1946.

9. Short, J. J. *A System of Weighed High Carbohydrate Diets for Diabetes.* J. Am. Med. Assoc. 96, 1940-1941, 1931.

10. Kramer, A. *The Nutritive Value of Canned Foods. VIII. Distribution of Proximate and Mineral Nutrients in the Drained and Liquid Portions of Canned Vegetables.* J. Am. Dietet. Assoc. 21, 354-356, 1945.

Chapter 2

PROTEINS AND AMINO ACIDS IN CANNED FOODS

Proteins are found in all cells. The proteins are hydrolyzed during digestion into amino acids; additional substances may be split off in the digestion of the so-called conjugated proteins, for example, nucleic acid from nucleoproteins. All evidence indicates the essential correctness of the idea advanced more than a century ago by Mülder, in his selection of the word "protein" to designate compounds which were of fundamental importance to living cells (1-3).

Proteins contain carbon, hydrogen, oxygen, nitrogen, sulfur, and sometimes phosphorus and small amounts of other elements. Despite the wide differences in the characteristics of proteins from different sources, it is remarkable how similar many different proteins are in elementary composition. Practically all proteins contain somewhat more than 50 per cent carbon; they also contain about 16 per cent nitrogen. The protein content of many foods is estimated by measuring their nitrogen content and multiplying the results by the factor 6.25. The data are sometimes designated in food tables as "Protein $(N \times 6.25)$". This factor has been used for converting into protein the data for the nitrogen content of canned foods, meat, eggs, corn, and most vegetable products. It is sometimes the practice to make use of other factors for certain foods because the nitrogen content of their proteins has been found to be slightly greater or less than 16 per cent. Thus, the factor suggested by Jones (4) for almonds is 5.18, for gelatin 5.55, and for milk 6.38. No practical difficulty arises with the use of the more commonly employed factor, 6.25, as long as it is so stated.

Proteins of Canned Foods

The data on the protein content of more than 200 canned foods are provided in Table I of the Appendix. Table VI of the Appendix includes a column to show the protein supplied by a serving of a limited number of canned foods, expressed as percentages of the daily recommended allowances for the physically active man. In Table X are shown the average protein content, in grams, of measured servings of canned foods.

These data show that the average protein content of canned foods is about the same as that of the products from which they are prepared. This would be anticipated, because there is no significant loss of protein in the canning of foods (5-7).

Foods richest in protein are the animal products, such as eggs, meat and meat products, fish, sea foods, poultry, milk, and milk products other than butter. The most important plant sources of proteins are nuts and other oily seeds, cereal grains, and leguminous vegetables such as peas and beans. A serving of canned green Lima beans (113 grams) provides 4.6 grams of protein. A serving of canned peas (113 grams) provides 4.0 grams, and a serving of canned baked beans (119 grams), 6.7 grams. These are significant contributions to the diet.

The nutritional value of proteins in foods varies with the nature of the food. It is higher as a rule in foods of animal origin than in those of plant origin. The biological value of a protein can be measured by feeding tests in which the efficiency of the protein is determined for maintenance or growth (8). Digestibility is an important factor in determining the biological value of proteins, but of greater importance is the composition of the protein in terms of its constituent amino acids.

Amino Acids

As already mentioned, proteins are converted into amino acids as a result of the successive action of the gastric, pancreatic and intestinal juices. These amino acids are absorbed into the blood and then transported to the liver and to all the tissues of the body, where they are resynthesized into protein, or consumed in metabolic processes. Regardless of the nature of the proteins of the diet, the proteins synthesized by the body cells are always characteristic of the tissue and of the species.

Nineteen amino acids may be obtained from ordinary proteins. The relative amounts of the individual amino acids are characteristic of each protein. It is owing to the pioneer work of Osborne and Mendel that differences in nutritive value of different proteins became recognized. By feeding diets containing pure protein preparations, they showed that the animal body is unable to synthesize certain amino acids, such as tryptophan and lysine, and growth is retarded unless these amino acids are included in the diet in adequate amounts. Other amino acids, such as aminoacetic acid (glycine), were found to be capable of being synthesized from other nitrogen sources. Hence, a distinction was made between essential and non-essential amino acids for the maintenance and growth of the rat.

An important contribution of these workers was the demonstration that the deficiency of an amino acid in one protein could be compensated for by the inclusion in the diet of other proteins which contained the essential amino acid. For example, in feeding experiments with rats, Osborne and Mendel (9) showed that a food mixture containing 4.5 per cent lactalbumin (from milk) and 13.5 per cent zein (from maize) would permit normal growth, whereas neither protein alone, in the quantities specified, was capable of supporting growth. The lactalbumin provided the essential amino acids, tryptophan and lysine, in which zein is deficient.

The nutritional properties of the individual amino acids have been studied experimentally by W. C. Rose and his students for many years. After their discovery and identification of a previously unknown amino acid, which they called

threonine, it was possible to obtain good growth in exper:
mental animals by feeding them a diet containing a mixtur
of all the amino acids in place of protein. By the successiv
removal of each amino acid it was possible to determine th
essential or non-essential nature of each of the amino acid:
The following amino acids were demonstrated to be nor
essential: Aminoacetic acid, alanine, serine, cystine, tyrosin
aspartic acid, glutamic acid, proline and hydroxyproline. I
was also demonstrated that the growing rat requires the fo:
lowing amino acids: Valine, leucine, isoleucine, threonin
methionine, lysine, phenlyalanine, tryptophan, histidine an
arginine. The absence from the diet of any of the ten esser
tial amino acids, except arginine, led to a loss of weight, dimir
ished appetite, nutritive failure and eventual death. In th
absence of arginine, growth was retarded, and this was ir
terpreted as an indication that the rat could synthesiz
arginine from other nitrogenous sources, but not at a rat
sufficient to supply the needs for normal growth.

In 1949, Rose reported (10) the results of several year:
work to determine the role of the individual amino acids i
the nutrition of man. Healthy male graduate students wer
selected for these experimental studies. They consumed a die
made from corn starch, sugar, butterfat, corn oil, inorgani
salts, and vitamins. This diet contained 0.35 gram or less c
nitrogen of unknown nature. Mixtures of purified amino acid
were taken in a solution flavored with filtered lemon juic
and sugar. The intake and excretion of nitrogen were deter
mined, and the maintenance of nitrogen equilibrium was take
as the measure of adequacy of the amino acid mixture.

In this manner it was shown that valine, leucine, isoleucin
threonine, methionine, lysine, phenylalanine, and tryptopha
are needed for the maintenance of nitrogen equilibrium i
young men. Arginine and histidine, which had been shown t
be needed for the growth of young rats, were found to be nor
essential for the maintenance of man. Rose wisely caution
that the amino acids needed for growth may differ from thos

eeded for maintenance. "Moreover," he has written, "one
annot yet exclude the possibility that certain amino acids
vhich are not necessary for nitrogen equilibrium in normal
ubjects under ordinary circumstances may become indispen-
able during disease, or for special body functions such as
etoxication, reproduction, or lactation" (10).

In a further series of remarkable experiments Rose and his
ollaborators have also studied the quantitative requirements
or each of the essential amino acids, and have provided data
or the minimum requirement, and the recommended daily
1take, for each of the eight essential amino acids. These data
n amino acid requirements are for healthy young men whose
iet furnishes sufficient nitrogen for the synthesis of the non-
ssential amino acids.

With this culmination of many years of painstaking experi-
1ents, and with the development of microbiological and other
1ethods for the reasonably accurate determination of indi-
idual amino acids in foods, a line of experimental investiga-
ion in which several outstanding protein chemists partici-
ated, it is likely that the science of Nutrition is entering upon
period of new understanding of the significance of protein
n health and disease.

mino Acid Content of Canned Fish and Meat Products

As part of its program to secure accurate quantitative infor-
1ation about the nutritional composition of canned foods
he canning industry sponsored two experimental studies of
he amino acid content of a number of canned foods which
ate as excellent sources of protein, such as canned fish and
1eat products. Also as part of its nutrition program, the
anning industry sponsored studies of the effects of the
anning process on the amino acid makeup of the proteins of
hese products. The results of these studies have been reported
y Dunn and associates (11) and by Neilands and his col-
aborators (12). The following canned products were studied:
:oast beef, whole boned ham, spiced ham, fish flakes, mackerel,

salmon, sardines in oil, sardines in tomato sauce, shrimp and tuna.

Amino acids—Microbiological methods were employed for the assay of the amino acids of the canned foods, and for each determination, a well mixed composite of several cans was used. The following thirteen amino acids were thus determined: Arginine, aspartic acid, glutamic acid, glycine, histidine, isoleucine, leucine, lysine, methionine, phenylalanine threonine, tryptophan and valine. The results of these determinations are provided in Table 5. It will be noted that the amino acids which were determined included all eight of the essential amino acids, plus several additional amino acids of proteins.

Retention of amino acids in canning—It was considered desirable to determine the effect of the canning process on the amino acid composition of the proteins of these canned foods. For this purpose, samples of raw fish or meat from the same lots used in preparing the processed samples were obtained, and their amino acid content determined and compared with the values obtained on the foods after canning. In a few instances also "precooked" samples were obtained as well, and analyzed.

The results of these retention studies are provided in Table 6. From these data the investigators concluded that, for the thirteen amino acids studied, there were no significant differences in the composition of these canned foods and of the raw materials from which they had been prepared, as shown by microbiological assay.

It was considered of interest to tabulate the composition of the canned meat products and fish, in terms of the amounts of the essential amino acids that would be provided by an average serving of these foods. The results of these computations are shown in Table XI of the Appendix, which also provides the tentative recommended daily intakes suggested by Rose (10) for the eight essential amino acids. The data for the amounts of the essential amino acids have been ex-

TABLE 5

Average Amino Acid Content of Canned Fish and Meat Samples

(Values given as per cent of protein N x 6.25)
Adapted from: Dunn et al. (11) and Neilands et al. (12)

Amino Acid	Atlantic Mackerel	Pacific Mackerel	Atlantic Sardines	Pacific Sardines	Fish Flakes	Shrimp *	Salmon	Spiced Ham	Whole Ham	Tuna	Beef
Arginine	5.7	5.2	5.5	5.0	6.2	9.4	5.7	6.1	6.4	5.2	6.0
Aspartic Acid	8.5	8.2	8.6	8.5	10.0	...	8.8	8.2	8.6	8.6	8.4
Glutamic Acid	12.2	12.8	12.9	12.2	14.8	...	12.8	14.4	14.5	12.9	14.0
Glycine	7.0	5.5	5.5	5.4	5.4	...	6.3	6.3	6.0	4.5	5.3
Histidine	3.6	5.2	2.2	4.5	2.1	2.2	2.5	3.1	3.4	5.9	3.5
Isoleucine	4.9	4.8	4.7	4.5	5.7	5.3	4.9	4.6	4.9	4.9	4.8
Leucine	7.3	7.4	7.2	7.2	8.1	8.5	7.4	7.7	7.9	7.3	7.6
Lysine	8.0	8.2	7.9	8.1	8.8	8.5	8.0	8.0	8.9	8.3	8.4
Methionine	2.8	2.8	2.7	2.8	3.0	3.4	3.1	2.4	2.5	2.8	2.6
Phenylalanine	3.4	3.8	3.6	3.7	3.8	4.5	3.7	3.7	3.8	3.7	3.6
Threonine	4.9	4.4	4.5	4.2	4.9	4.1	4.4	4.0	4.2	4.3	4.4
Tryptophan	1.0	1.0	0.8	1.0	1.0	1.0	0.9	0.8	1.0	0.9	0.9
Valine	5.2	5.2	5.1	5.2	5.4	5.1	5.6	4.9	5.4	5.3	5.0

* Drained, only solid portion analyzed.

TABLE 6

Amino Acid Content of Fish and Meat Products Before and After Heat Processing

(Values given as per cent of protein, N x 6.25)

Adapted from: Dunn et al. (11) and Neilands et al. (12)

Amino Acid	Atlantic Mackerel		Pacific Mackerel		Atlantic Sardines		Pacific Sardines			Fish Flakes	
	Raw	Canned	Raw	Canned	Raw	Canned	Raw	Prec. †	Canned	Raw	Canned
Arginine	5.6	5.8	5.6	5.5	5.7	5.6	5.5		4.9	6.1	6.0
Arginine	5.7	5.7	5.3	5.6	5.4	5.8	4.8	(5.4)	4.9	5.9	6.3
Aspartic Acid	9.2	9.3	9.0	8.3	7.7	9.2	9.2		8.0	10.2	9.8
Aspartic Acid	9.2	9.0	9.0	8.5			8.9	(9.6)	8.8	9.0	10.1
Glutamic Acid	13.1	13.3	12.8	13.0	11.2	13.2	13.2		11.3	15.2	14.6
Glutamic Acid	13.2	12.4	12.8	12.8			11.5	(13.5)	12.0	13.6	15.1
Glycine	5.7	7.0	5.6	5.3	5.3	6.4	6.6		5.6	5.2	5.0
Glycine	6.2	6.7	5.8	5.4			5.2	(5.8)	4.9	4.6	5.7
Histidine	4.2	3.7	5.2	5.1	2.6	2.4	5.1		4.7	2.1	2.1
Histidine	3.9	3.6	5.8	5.3	2.4	2.4	4.6	(4.9)	4.3	1.9	2.0
Isoleucine	5.3	5.2	4.7	5.8	5.1	5.3	4.7		4.4	5.7	5.5
Isoleucine	5.3	5.1	4.9	4.8	4.6	4.9	4.9	(4.9)	4.5	5.4	5.7
Leucine	7.0	7.3	7.7	7.5	7.2	7.2	7.4		7.3	8.3	8.0
Leucine	7.1	7.0	7.4	7.2	6.7	7.4	7.4	(8.0)	7.3	7.7	8.2
Lysine	8.3	8.4	9.1	8.3	8.1	7.8	8.8		8.5	9.3	9.1
Lysine	8.1	8.2	8.5	8.7	7.6	8.2	8.5	(9.5)	8.1	8.7	9.1
Methionine	2.7	2.7	2.8	2.9	2.9	2.5	2.7		2.7	3.1	2.9
Methionine	2.7	2.7	2.8	2.8	2.6	2.9	2.7	(3.0)	2.9	3.0	3.1
Phenylalanine	3.6	3.6	4.1	3.8	3.3	3.6	4.0		3.6	3.9	3.7
Phenylalanine	3.5	3.4	3.8	3.9	3.4	3.6	3.7	(4.0)	3.8	3.7	4.0
Threonine	5.1	5.5	4.3	4.4	4.0	4.2	4.5		3.9	5.2	5.1
Threonine	4.4	5.1	4.6	4.5	4.6	4.6	4.4	(4.9)	4.1	4.9	5.3
Tryptophan	0.9	0.9	1.1	1.0	0.8	0.8	1.0		1.1	1.1	1.0
Tryptophan	0.9	0.3	1.1	1.1	0.8	0.8	1.0	(1.1)	1.1	1.0	1.0
Valine	5.7	5.3	5.5	5.3	5.3	5.4	5.2		5.2	5.5	5.3
Valine	5.6	5.3	5.2	5.1	4.7	5.2	5.2	(5.6)	5.5	5.0	5.5

Amino Acid Content of Fish and Meat Products Before and After Heat Processing

(Values given as per cent of protein, N x 6.25)

Adapted from: Dunn et al. (11) and Neilands et al. (12)

Amino Acid	Salmon		Tuna		Roast Beef		Whole Ham		Spiced Ham	
	Raw	Canned	Raw	Prec.†	Raw	Canned	Raw	Canned	Raw	Canned
Arginine	5.7	5.7	5.2	(5.2)	6.1	6.1	6.1	6.2	6.2	5.9
Arginine	5.8	5.5	5.5	(5.1)			6.6	6.6	6.4	6.3
Aspartic Acid	9.1	9.0	8.3	(8.8)	9.2	8.4	9.1	8.6	8.7	7.7
Aspartic Acid	9.3	8.8	8.4	(8.4)			9.5	8.7	8.9	8.5
Glutamic Acid	13.2	13.0	13.0	(13.6)	15.1	14.0	14.8	14.4	14.3	13.1
Glutamic Acid	13.6	12.6	11.4	(11.8)			15.5	14.6	15.8	15.8
Glycine	6.0	6.4	4.6	(4.3)	5.3	5.3	6.2	6.0	6.8	6.1
Glycine	6.2	5.8	6.1	(5.0)			5.9	5.9	6.4	6.8
Histidine	2.7	2.7	5.7	(5.9)	3.8	3.5	3.7	3.5	2.9	2.8
Histidine	2.5	2.4	5.8	(5.3)			3.5	3.4	3.1	3.2
Isoleucine	5.1	5.0	4.3	(4.6)	5.2	4.9	4.8	4.8	4.4	4.4
Isoleucine	4.9	4.8	4.6	(5.0)			5.0	5.0	4.7	4.8
Leucine	7.0	7.4	6.8	(7.1)	8.0	7.6	7.8	7.8	7.5	7.5
Leucine	7.3	7.1	7.1	(7.2)			8.0	8.0	8.0	7.7
Lysine	8.0	8.3	8.0	(8.7)	8.9	8.4	8.7	9.0	8.6	7.8
Lysine	8.3	8.0	8.5	(8.1)			9.1	8.8	8.3	8.2
Methionine	2.9	3.1	2.8	(2.8)	2.7	2.6	2.4	2.5	2.4	2.2
Methionine	3.1	2.9	2.9	(2.8)			2.8	2.6	2.5	2.4
Phenylalanine	3.6	3.7	3.3	(3.5)	4.0	3.6	3.7	3.6	3.8	3.6
Phenylalanine	3.8	3.5	3.5	(3.6)			3.9	3.7	4.0	3.7
Threonine	4.0	4.6	4.1	(4.6)	4.7	4.4	4.2	4.2	4.3	3.9
Threonine	4.4	4.6	5.4	(4.6)			4.3	4.2	4.4	4.3
Tryptophan	0.9	0.9	1.1	(1.1)	1.1	0.9	1.0	0.9	0.9	0.9
Tryptophan	1.0	0.9	1.0	(1.0)			1.1	1.1	0.9	0.8
Valine	5.6	5.7	4.8	(5.0)	5.4	5.0	5.3	5.4	4.9	4.8
Valine	5.5	5.4	5.3	(5.4)			5.5	5.4	5.2	5.0

† "Precooked"

pressed in terms of percentages of the recommended daily intakes.

While calculations of this sort are only suggestive, in view of the present state of knowledge, the data do serve to emphasize the acknowledged high nutritive quality of the proteins of these canned foods. A single serving of any of these foods provides substantial quantities of all of the essential amino acids, as well as of the total protein needs of the adult. Particularly notable are the high proportions of the requirements which canned fish provide with respect to isoleucine, lysine, and threonine.

REFERENCES

1. American Medical Association, Council on Foods and Nutrition. *Handbook on Nutrition*, Chapter II. Am. Med. Assoc., Chicago, 1943.
2. United States Dept. of Agriculture. *Food and Life, Yearbook of Agriculture 1939.* U. S. Gov't Printing Office, Washington, D. C., 173-186, 1939.
3. McCollum, E. V., Orent-Keiles, E. and Day, H. G. *The Newer Knowledge of Nutrition, 5th Ed.* Macmillan Company, New York, 1939.
4. Jones, D. B. *Factors for Converting Percentage of Nitrogen in Foods and Feeds into Percentages of Proteins.* U. S. Dept. of Agr. Circ. 183, 1931.
5. Morgan, A. F. and Kern, G. E. *Effect of Heat Upon the Biological Value of Meat Protein.* J. Nutrition 7, 367-379, 1934.
6. Robinson, H. E. *The Effect of Heat on the Dietary Value of Meat Proteins.* The Canner 80, No. 9, 102-103, 1935.
7. Melnick, D. and Oser, B. L. *The Influence of Heat Processing on the Functional and Nutritive Properties of Protein.* Food Technology 3, 57-71, 1949.
8. *Measuring the Biologic Value of Proteins.* Nutrition Revs. 2, 169-171, 1944.
9. Osborne, T. B. and Mendel, L. B. *Nutritive Properties of Proteins of the Maize Kernel.* J. Biol. Chem. 18, 1-16, 1914.
10. Rose, W. C. *Amino Acid Requirements of Man.* Federation Proc. 8, 546-552, 1949.
11. Dunn, M. S., Camien, M. N., Eiduson, S. and Malin, R. B. *XXXIII. The Nutritive Value of Canned Foods I. Amino Acid Content of Fish and Meat Products.* J. Nutrition 39, 177-185, 1949.
12. Nielands, J. B., Sirny, R. J., Sohljell, I., Strong, F. M. and Elvehjem, C. A. *XXXIII. The Nutritive Value of Canned Foods II. Amino Acid Content of Fish and Meat Products.* J. Nutrition 39, 187-202, 1949.

Chapter 3

THE MINERALS OF CANNED FOODS

When foods are burned all the organic materials are consumed and there is left an ash. When this process is performed under controlled conditions the weight of the inorganic residue provides the figure for the ash content of the material examined, and is so recorded in the proximate analysis of a food. Although all body tissues and fluids contain some inorganic salts, some tissues such as bones and teeth have long been known to yield considerable ash. Early in the history of Nutrition the significance of foods as contributors of inorganic salts to the skeletal tissues of the body was recognized. Before the time of Lavoisier the presence of sufficient iron in blood to yield a reddish color of ferric oxide in the ash was known. The concept developed that particular elements are especially important in the structure, and presumably in the function, of body tissues and organs.

It is now known that the inorganic elements, or minerals, of foods, as well as of the body, may be conveniently divided into three categories (1):

1. *The major inorganic elements.* These are the base-forming elements, calcium, magnesium, sodium, and potassium, and the acid forming elements, phosphorus, chlorine and sulfur. They not only make up the bulk of the ash of biological materials, as a rule, but they function importantly in the structure and physiology of the body, and their salts are the chief regulators of the acid-base balance of body tissues and fluids.
2. *The essential elements needed in small quantities.* Among these elements which are essential to life, iron and iodine have long been known. Iron is a component of the hemoglobin or red coloring matter of blood, and it is present in other organic compounds which are found in the tissues. Iodine is a component of thyroxin, the hormone produced by the thyroid gland. During the last twenty-five years the following elements also have been demonstrated to be significant in the nutrition of animals, and in small amounts are considered of probable sig-

nificance in human nutrition: Cobalt, copper, fluorine, manganese and zinc.

3. *Trace elements of unknown significance.* These include elements such as aluminum, bromine, nickel, and silicon. The presence of traces of these elements as well as others in foods and body tissues may be purely adventitious. It should be recognized, however, that the essential trace elements, such as copper, were in this category until investigations revealed their importance in the physiology of the body.

Functions of the Inorganic Elements

The functions of the minerals known to be essential in the human body may be conveniently classified as follows:

1. To give structural strength and support to the skeletal tissues such as bones and teeth.
2. To assist in the maintenance of normal osmotic pressure, and of acid-base balance of the body, to assist also in the regulation of heart beat, and the maintenance of normal neuromuscular irritability.
3. To serve as components of important compounds of muscle, blood and other tissue cells, enzyme and hormone systems, and body pigments.

Calcium and phosphorus—The strength and rigidity of the bones and teeth, as already mentioned, are owing to the deposition of minerals in these tissues, chiefly calcium phosphate. Calcium ions are involved in the clotting of the blood, the regulation of the heart beat, the maintenance of acid-base balance in the body, and the irritability of the neuromuscular system. Phosphorus functions as the phosphate radical. The phosphates are among the principal buffers of the blood and other body fluids, and serve, along with proteins and bicarbonates, in regulating the hydrogen ion concentration of the body. Phosphates occur in all cells of the body. Several of the vitamins function in the form of phosphates, as components of enzyme systems that make possible oxidation of foodstuffs in the cells. Phosphorus also enters into the composition of phospholipids which have important functions in physiology. Phosphorus and calcium are closely related in their metabolism, and both in turn are influenced by vitamin D and the parathyroid hormone.

The chief sources of calcium and phosphorus in the diet are milk and milk products other than butter. Certain marine products, particularly canned fish, and green leafy and other vegetables are also significant sources of calcium. The calcium of some vegetable foods, such as spinach, is largely unavailable because it is combined as insoluble calcium oxalate, although these foods are important because of their content of other nutrients. Whole grain cereal foods are rich in phosphorus, but much of this phosphorus is in the form of phytic acid, and is not completely available to the body.

Courtesy Continental Can Company, Inc.

Photometric technics help speed the estimation of trace elements in canned foods.

Sodium and chlorine—It is customary to consider sodium and chlorine together, as sodium chloride. The universal practice of salting foods to taste is in general a satisfactory means of supplying the needs for these elements in nutrition. Salt functions in the maintenance of osmotic pressure of body fluids, and the chloride is the source of the hydrochloric acid of the gastric juice. Salt always exists in the body in solution, and it is eliminated in solution largely by the kidneys. This process involves work by the kidneys and by the heart.

There is no problem in obtaining sufficient salt to meet the needs of the body. There is a problem concerned with the formulation of therapeutic diets that are low in sodium, as in the dietary management of hypertension (2), because of the practice of seasoning foods in processing or in preparation in the home. Some natural foods, such as milk, also contain appreciable amounts of sodium. For persons who are restricted by their physicians to low-sodium foods, special unsalted foods have been made available. Canned salt-free vegetables, and water-packed and juice-packed fruits have been found to be useful because of their low content of sodium.

Other major food minerals: Potassium, magnesium and sulphur.—Potassium is found, like sodium, in the body fluids but, unlike sodium, it tends to be found in higher concentrations within the body cells. Magnesium is found associated with calcium and phosphate in the inorganic material of bones and teeth. Both potassium and magnesium function to a minor extent in acid-base and osmotic relationships of the body fluids. Sulfur is also concerned with the acid-base balance of the body, because it is eliminated as sulfate. Apparently, the only form in which the body can utilize sulfur is in the form of the organic sulfur compounds, such as the amino acids, methionine and cystine. Methionine has been shown to be an essential amino acid to man. Some of the vitamins essential in the diet contain sulfur in their molecules.

As far as is known, sufficient quantities of potassium and magnesium are provided by ordinary diets of mixed foods.

The requirements for sulfur are supplied by methionine, or other essential organic compounds of sulfur and hence are part of the protein or the vitamin story of nutrition.

Iron—Iron is a component of certain compounds which are concerned with oxidations within the body cells, and of hemoglobin, which transports oxygen from the lungs to all parts of the body. Except for the production of hemoglobin, the requirements for iron appear to be readily met by the iron content of ordinary diets. It is necessary to give consideration, however, to the iron content of the dietary of all persons who are growing or producing new tissue or blood. The iron requirements are higher per unit weight, during infancy, childhood and adolescence, in pregnancy, and for women during the child-bearing period, and for all persons following blood loss. Although simple iron deficiency of the diet may result in one form of anemia, there are other anemias which are not related to iron deficiency.

There is evidence that different forms of iron vary in their availability to the body, the simple iron salts being most effective. The dietary standards have been established high enough so that, for most purposes, the total iron content of foods may be considered to contribute to the nutritional requirements. Among the important food sources of iron are meats, sardines and other sea foods, many vegetables especially the green, leafy vegetables, poultry and eggs, whole grain and enriched cereals, and dried legumes.

Iodine—Very small amounts of iodine are required for the production of thyroxin, but these amounts are not always assured by the foods or drinking water consumed in many areas of the country. In the absence of a sufficient intake of iodine, endemic goiter may result. It has been shown that this deficiency disease can be effectively controlled by the use of iodized salt. Health authorities have recommended the universal iodization of all salt intended for use in the home preparation of foods, and have recommended its regular use by persons of all ages.

Essential trace elements: Cobalt, copper, fluorine, manganese and zinc—Small amounts of cobalt salts under certain conditions may stimulate the production of red blood cells in experimental animals. Sheep, cattle and other ruminants exhibit profound nutritive failure when maintained on feed that has been grown in soils deficient in this element, and they are protected by administration of cobalt salts. With the discovery that cobalt is a component of the vitamin B_{12} molecule (3), it may be anticipated that the functions of this element in human nutrition will receive further intensive study.

Copper has been shown to be needed to enable the body to convert simple iron salts into hemoglobin. Manganese is necessary for the growth of both plants and animals. There is evidence that traces of zinc are important in the growth of experimental animals, and insulin, the hormone of the pancreas, can be isolated as the zinc salt.

Fluorine occurs in the form of an inorganic salt in bones and teeth. Its importance from the nutritional point of view is under experimental investigation. While small amounts of fluorine appear to be essential, larger amounts may be harmful. In communities where the fluorine content of the drinking water exceeds 1.5 parts per million, mottling of the enamel of the permanent teeth of young children frequently is encountered (4). On the other hand, there is evidence that the presence of fluorine in drinking water to the extent of 0.5 to about 1.5 parts per million may be beneficial in the control of dental caries. In several communities experimental studies are being made of the possible value of adding small amounts of fluorides to drinking water, in the prevention of tooth decay of growing children.

In general it is considered likely that any human needs for these important trace elements are met by diets of ordinary foods.

Nutritional Needs for Minerals

As has been mentioned, dietary allowances have been established for calcium and iron. The requirements for phosphorus, as also has been pointed out, usually are met when the calcium requirements are provided for, because foods which are important sources of calcium are also outstanding sources of phosphorus. The requirements for iodine can be met by the regular use of iodized table salt. Experimental work on the needs for other elements may be considered to be in progress.

A number of useful tables of minerals in common foods are available, and perhaps the best known of these is the compilation by Sherman (5). The table by Bridges (6) is widely used, and other useful compilations are available (7-9).

The experimental work of the canned food nutrition program has been concerned with the total ash, and the calcium, phosphorus and iron contents of canned foods. The effects of processing, and the distribution of mineral nutrients between solid and liquid contents of the can were also studied.

Mineral Composition of Canned Foods

In Table I of the Appendix are provided the ash content of more than 200 different canned foods. Data on the amounts of calcium, phosphorus and iron in the products examined in the canned food nutrition program, as determined by Kramer (10) are provided in Table II of the Appendix. Table VI shows the contribution of calcium and iron provided in typical servings of canned foods, in terms of proportions of the recommended dietary allowances. The actual amounts of calcium, phosphorus and iron contained in servings of canned foods are provided in Table X of the Appendix.

Calcium—While all canned foods were found to contain some calcium, and therefore capable of contributing to the extent of their composition to the dietary requirements for this essential, a number of products were found to contain significant amounts. Canned fish in particular are good food sources of calcium. The approximate calcium content of a number of canned foods, as classified by Kramer (10) is shown in Table 7.

TABLE 7

Approximate Calcium Content of Some Canned Foods

Adapted from: Kramer (10)

Approximate Calcium Content mg. per 100 g.	Canned Food	
350	Sardines	
200	Mackerel	Salmon
100	Shrimp, dry pack	Turnip greens
	Spinach	
50	Beans, baked	Shrimp, wet pack
40	Beans, green	Kraut
	Beans, Lima	Pineapple, sliced
	Carrots	Sweetpotatoes

The data in Table 7 were obtained by analyzing the entire contents of the cans. Most fruits and vegetable products contain 10 or less milligrams of calcium per 100 grams and are not significant food sources of this dietary essential.

Phosphorus—The canned foods which were found to be significant sources of calcium were also found, as a rule, to supply relatively high amounts of phosphorus. In Table 8 are shown the approximate amounts of phosphorus found in a number of canned foods, as determined by Kramer (10).

Iron—The iron content of canned foods reflects the iron content of the foods from which they are prepared. The data obtained reveal considerable variation, as has been observed for the same foods in the raw state. Considering only the minimum values obtained in the canned food nutrition studies, the following foods all may be expected to contain 1.3 milligrams of iron, or more, to each 100 grams: Baked beans, Lima beans, blueberries, cherries, white corn (whole grain), kraut, mackerel, peppers, sardines, shrimp, and turnip greens.

TABLE 8

Approximate Phosphorus Content of Some Canned Foods

Adapted from: Kramer (10)

Approximate Phosphorus Content mg. per 100 g.	Canned Food	
400	Sardines, in oil	
300	Mackerel	Salmon
225	Shrimp, dry pack	Tuna
175	Sardines, in tomato sauce	Shrimp, wet pack
100	Beans, baked	
65	Beans, Lima	Corn, vacuum pack
	Corn, yellow, whole grain	Peas
	Corn, cream style	Mushrooms
		Sweetpotatoes
45	Asparagus, green	Corn, white, whole grain

Distribution Studies

The results of Kramer's studies (11) of the distribution of calcium, phosphorus and iron between solids and liquids in the contents of the canned foods examined are summarized in Table 9. With the exception of spinach, as shown in the Table, at least 11 per cent of the total calcium was found to be present in the liquid portion of the products examined. The low value for calcium dissolved from spinach may be attributed to the formation of insoluble calcium oxalate (12). It was also found that the iron of spinach was retained in the solid portion of the contents of the can to a greater extent than was observed in the case of other foods.

About 11 per cent of the iron of canned spinach was found in the liquid portion, whereas 24 per cent or more of the iron of other foods was found in the liquid. About 19 per cent or more of the phosphorus of the canned foods examined was found in the liquid portion.

These facts lend emphasis to the repeated injunction, that to obtain the full nutritive value of canned foods, it is well to make use of the liquid portion of the contents of the can.

TABLE 9

Percentage of Total Minerals in Liquid Portion of Canned Foods

Adapted from: Kramer (11)

Canned Food	Average Percentages		
	Calcium	Iron	Phosphorus
Asparagus	30	27	19
Green beans	17	24	27
Lima beans	28	32	28
Beets	11	25	31
Carrots	17	33	24
Corn, whole grain	23	27	30
Peas	17	28	26
Spinach	0.7	11	28

The use of blanching in canning operations is restricted to certain of the common vegetables which are later packed in a liquid containing salt, sugar, or both, and heat-processed after the can is sealed (peas, green beans, Lima beans, asparagus, and spinach). It is likely that the loss of water-soluble minerals during the blanching operation would be considerably less than the transfer of these same nutrients from the solid portion to the liquid portion of the contents of the can during heat processing and subsequent storage. This is because the time and temperature are much more conducive to extraction of soluble nutrients during heat processing than during the blanching operation. Peas, for example, are commonly blanched for about four to seven minutes in water maintained at 180° to 200° F. During the sterilization process, however, about 13-14 ounces of the peas with six to seven fluid ounces of water are heated in a sealed No. 2 can for 35 minutes at 240° F.

Kramer and Smith (13) found that the blanching of peas, green beans, Lima beans, and spinach resulted in slight losses in ash and phosphorus and, frequently, moderate increases in calcium content.

REFERENCES

1. Shohl, A. T. *Mineral Metabolism.* Reinhold Publishing Co., New York, 1939.
2. Editorial. *Dietary Therapy of Hypertension.* J. Am. Med. Assoc. 137, 147-148, 1948.
3. Rickes, E. L., Brink, N. G., Koniuszy, F. R., Wood, T. R., and Folkers, K. *Vitamin B₁₂, a Cobalt Complex.* Science 108, 134, 1948.
4. American Medical Association, Council on Foods and Nutrition. *Handbook of Nutrition.* Am. Med. Assoc., Chicago, 1943.
5. Sherman, H. C. *Chemistry of Food and Nutrition, 7th Ed.* Macmillan Co., New York, 1946.
6. Bridges, M. A. *Dietetics for the Clinician, 4th Ed.* Lea & Febiger, Philadelphia, 1941.
7. *Tables of Food Composition in Terms of Eleven Nutrients.* U. S. Dept. Agr. Misc. Pub's. 572, 1945.
8. Clouse, R. C. *Compilation of Recent Data on Mineral and Vitamin Values of Food.* J. Am. Dietet. Assoc. 18, 553-561, 1942.
9. Clouse, R. C. *Compilation of Recent Data on Mineral and Vitamin Values of Foods.* J. Am. Dietet. Assoc. 19, 746-755, 1943.
10. Kramer, A. *Nutritive Value of Canned Foods. XVI. Proximate and Mineral Composition.* Food Research 11, 391-398, 1946.
11. Kramer, A. *The Nutritive Value of Canned Foods. VIII. Distribution of Proximate and Mineral Nutrients in the Drained and Liquid Portions of Canned Vegetables.* J. Am. Dietet. Assoc. 21, 354-356, 1945.
12. *Effects of Oxalic Acid in the Diet.* Nutrition Revs. 3, 324-325, 1945.
13. Kramer, A. and Smith, M. H. *Nutritive Value of Canned Foods. XXIV. Effect of Duration and Temperature of Blanch on Proximate and Mineral Composition of Certain Vegetables.* Ind. Eng. Chem. 39, 1007-1009, 1947.

Chapter 4

ASCORBIC ACID IN CANNED FOODS*

Ascorbic acid, or vitamin C, is the factor which prevents or cures scurvy. Ascorbic acid was isolated from rich natural sources in 1932, its structure determined in 1933 and, in the same year, its synthesis accomplished. Ascorbic acid can be considered as a derivative of a sugar. It is identified chemically as a lactone of keto-gulonic acid. The vitamin exists in at least two biologically active forms: Ascorbic acid and dehydro-ascorbic acid.

Ascorbic acid is necessary for the production by the body of the organic portion of the structure of bones and teeth, as well as the organic framework of many of the softer tissues of the body. For this reason ascorbic acid is peculiarly important in bone and tooth formation and the healing of wounds. It is involved in the maintenance of normal healthy conditions of the gums and oral cavity, and it is involved in the maintenance of normal capillary structure and function.

Ascorbic acid apparently is important in plant metabolism for it is widely distributed in both edible and inedible plant materials. The extent to which this vitamin is found in plant tissues may be quite variable. Within the same plant ascorbic acid may be present in greater concentration in certain tissues than in others. Likewise, differences in ascorbic acid content will be found in the same portions of different plants. These variations have been repeatedly noted in raw food materials selected for canning. As an example, in Table 10 are listed

---

* Ascorbic acid in canned foods is considered at this point because, historically, the first nutrition studies supported by the National Canners Association were concerned with this vitamin; since that time many data on the vitamin C content of canned foods have been obtained and consideration of these data provides a convenient basis for comparison of data about other vitamins of canned foods, which is the subject of succeeding chapters.

ascorbic acid values of raw canning peas as reported by Alexander and Feaster (1).

TABLE 10

Ascorbic Acid in Raw Peas

Adapted from: Alexander and Feaster (1)

Variety	Sieve Size	Ascorbic Acid Contents mg./100 g.
Alaska	1-4	27-60
Pride	2-7	21-66
Profusion	3-7	16-22
Perfection	1-6	20-33
Pennin	4-7	17-25
Alderman	4-7	21-28

All the factors influencing these natural variations in the initial vitamin content of raw food materials are not known, but variety, maturity, growing locality, and growing conditions are recognized as important.

The pure vitamin is water-soluble and easily oxidized, with loss of vitamin potency, but it is relatively stable to heat in the absence of oxygen.

Ascorbic Acid Retentions During Canning

Fruits, vegetables, and their related products constitute the major food sources of ascorbic acid. In the commercial canning of these products, conditions of extraction and oxidation may exist which in the early days of vitamin research aroused question as to the extent to which ascorbic acid would be affected by canning operations. In the canned food nutrition program considerable study was devoted to the retention of this vitamin in a wide variety of foods. These studies on ascorbic acid retention were of two general types: The "over-all" retentions which reflect the degree of vitamin conservation during the sequence of operations required to convert the raw food material to the finished canned product, and the "step-by-step" retentions which measured the degree of vitamin conservation during the individual preparatory operations.

Retention During Blanching—Comprehensive and detailed data on vitamin retention during blanching, an operation known to affect ascorbic acid, and over-all vitamin retentions during canning are to be found in publications of Guerrant *et al.* (2, 3), Wagner and associates (4, 5), and Lamb *et al.* (6). These findings were recently summarized by Cameron *et al.* (7) who presented the trends of the results on typical products.

The specific effects of blanching on ascorbic acid retention are shown in Figure 7. As indicated by the parenthetical figures, the amount of available data varies from 12 observations for ascorbic acid during blanching for Lima beans to 60 for peas. Where 30 or more observations were available, frequency distributions were calculated and the bar graphs shown represent the figures within which 90 per cent of the observations were found to fall. Asparagus, green beans, Lima beans, peas, and spinach are the major canned food commodities which are subjected to hot-water blanching during preparation and the blanch schedules employed vary over a wide range of time and temperature.

From the standpoint of the mean ascorbic acid retentions shown in Figure 7, these data show that substantial retentions of this vitamin may be realized under commercial operating conditions. The best retention was noted in the case of asparagus (mean, 95 per cent) while the lowest and most variable retention was that of spinach (mean, 67 per cent). These variations are attributable to the relatively small surface areas of asparagus combined with the short blanch customarily used for this product. In contrast, spinach is a product with a thin, extensive surface area which presents greater opportunity for solution of water-soluble ascorbic acid. The range of ascorbic acid retention in spinach during blanching is also quite broad, varying from a minimum of less than 10 per cent to a maximum of more than 90 per cent with a mean value of 67 per cent. This wide range is believed due in no small part to the variations in blanching practices to which the samples included in these studies had been subjected.

FIGURE 7. Ascorbic Acid Retentions during Blanching

Adapted from: Cameron et al. (7)

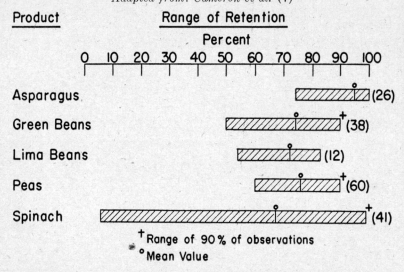

While the results shown in Figure 7 indicate that improvement from the standpoint of ascorbic acid retention may still be effected, the mean and maximum retentions listed also suggest that the serious concern expressed by some earlier workers over the possibility of almost complete ascorbic acid extraction during blanching is not justified.

Over-All Retentions. The studies previously described (3-6) determined over-all ascorbic retentions for the following canned foods:

Grapefruit juice	Corn	Tomatoes
Peas	Lima beans	Tomato juice
Asparagus	Orange juice	Spinach
Green beans	Carrots	Apricots
Wax beans	Cherries	Peaches

Concerning these and related studies, the summary shown in Figure 8 was recently presented for selected foods subjected to a variety of operations during canning (7).

FIGURE 8.   Over-all Ascorbic Acid Retentions

Adapted from: Cameron et al. (7)

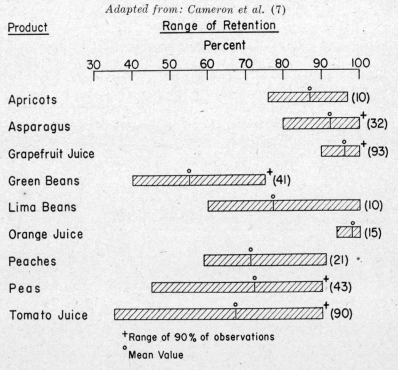

These data indicate that retention varies with the product and that raw products significantly high in ascorbic acid remain significant sources after canning. The results obtained for asparagus and the citrus juices show very high retentions of this nutrient, the mean retentions being more than 90 per cent. For tomato juice it is evident from Figure 8 that retention varied over a wide range. This was also the case with products subjected to relatively severe blanching procedures (green beans, Lima beans, peas, and spinach). The lower values shown for tomato juice are believed to be associated with incorporaton of air in the juice and holding while warm for an appreciable period during preparation.

Protective Influences—These findings on ascorbic acid retention indicate that the properties and stability of the pure vitamin do not always reflect the behavior of ascorbic acid in complex natural systems as exist in foods. There is also evidence that besides the natural protection afforded ascorbic acid, other factors operate during commercial canning to explain the high retentions indicated in Figure 8. Among these may be listed: Rapid handling of the raw material after harvesting, prompt heat inactivation or destruction of oxidative enzymes or enzyme systems, and maximum protection from atmospheric oxygen. More specifically, the raw food products are usually handled in a speedy fashion to avoid as far as possible any changes between harvesting and the completion of the canning operation. As soon as a product has been severed from its parent root, enzymatic processes are set in action which promote the oxidation of many constituents in the plant itself, among these being ascorbic acid. Fracturing, chopping, shelling, or any other operation which disrupts the cell walls and activates enzymes, also catalyzes the oxidation of ascorbic acid.

In modern canning procedures, these adverse influences are controlled either by inactivation of the enzymes by heat in the preparatory operations or by the rapidity with which raw foods are transformed into the final canned products. Best retentions are obtained with minimum time lapse between harvesting and completion of the canning operation.

Ascorbic Acid Content of Canned Foods

In Table III of the Appendix are listed the ascorbic acid contents of commercially canned foods as determined in studies sponsored by the canned foods nutrition program (8, 9). Data on the ascorbic acid content of more than 40 commercially canned foods which are produced and consumed in large quantities each year are provided. This Table indicates the product, the number of samples considered, and the maximum, minimum, and average ascorbic acid values found based on the entire contents (liquids, or solids and liquid) in the can. In certain of the products, large variations between the minimum and maximum ascorbic acid values are to be noted. These variations are due both to the natural factors already described, and in some instances to variations in the commercial procedures employed in the canning of these products.

To provide a ready and convenient basis of comparison, the average data on ascorbic acid contents in commercially canned foods from Table III have been shown graphically in Figure 9. As will be noted, the products are listed in descending order of ascorbic acid content. These values are on a 100 gram (3.5 ounces) basis.

Distribution Between Solid and Liquid Phases

Provision was made in the canned food nutrition program for determination of the distribution of ascorbic acid between the solid and liquid portions of the canned products in the case of foods packed as solids in liquids. Although most of the ascorbic acid present was associated with the solid portion of the can contents, the liquid portion also contained appreciable amounts of this vitamin. These studies show that the liquids in which such foods are packed acquire appreciable amounts of water-soluble nutrients and hence could well be saved and used.

Application to Human Nutrition

To illustrate the values of commercially canned foods in practical problems of human nutrition, Table X of the Appendix has been prepared. This Table lists for more than 40 canned foods the approximate size of servings as determined by the Home Economics Division of the National Canners

FIGURE 9

Ascorbic Acid Content of Canned Foods

Combined data from 1942 and 1943 Phase I surveys

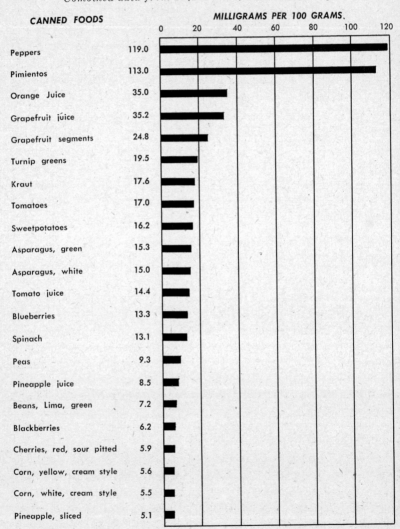

FIGURE 9 (Continued)

Ascorbic Acid Content of Canned Foods

Combined data from 1942 and 1943 Phase I surveys

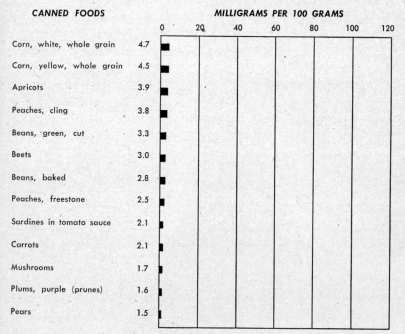

CANNED FOODS		MILLIGRAMS PER 100 GRAMS
Corn, white, whole grain	4.7	
Corn, yellow, whole grain	4.5	
Apricots	3.9	
Peaches, cling	3.8	
Beans, green, cut	3.3	
Beets	3.0	
Beans, baked	2.8	
Peaches, freestone	2.5	
Sardines in tomato sauce	2.1	
Carrots	2.1	
Mushrooms	1.7	
Plums, purple (prunes)	1.6	
Pears	1.5	

Association and the amount of the various nutritive factors contained in such servings. The proportion of recommended daily allowances (Food and Nutrition Board, National Research Council) and minimum daily requirements (Food and Drug Administration) represented by these amounts are shown in Tables VI and VII of the Appendix.

The figures in the column for ascorbic acid present at a glance the relative values of the various fruits, juices, and vegetables with respect to this vitamin and indicate their respective contributions to the daily allowance. It will be seen that many of these foods are highly significant sources of ascorbic acid. Likewise, the frequency with which these foods are included in the diet is a factor which must be considered in estimating their value as contributors of this vitamin.

Future Improvements

One approach to improvement of nutritive levels in all processed foods lies in the modification of existing procedures, and in more effective operation of present equipment. With respect to greater ascorbic acid retention in canned foods, Wagner *et al.* (5) and Guerrant *et al.* (2) have shown by controlled experiments that alterations in certain commercial blanch schedules (high-temperature short-time blanches rather than long-time blanches at either high or low temperatures) may favor retention of this vitamin in some canned foods. Recently, in other studies sponsored under the canned foods nutrition program, Lamb *et al.* (10), Feaster and associates (11), Heberlein *et al.* (12) have confirmed these findings with respect to peas. By alteration of existing cannery blanch schedules it is possible to demonstrate on a production scale that ascorbic acid retention can be distinctly improved. Similar applications of other new findings to other food products are also anticipated.

Apart from future improvement in existing canning techniques which may favor ascorbic acid retention in canned foods, there exists considerable promise of increasing the final ascorbic acid levels of canned products through production of raw food materials with higher initial content of this vitamin than those now commonly used. There appear to be two general approaches to improvement of raw canning stocks; either through improved cultural methods or research in plant genetics. Studies of this type are currently in progress (13-15). Students of nutrition may thus be assured that with this interest and with the work that is going on, further improvements in nutritive quality will result.

REFERENCES

1. Alexander, O. R. and Feaster, J. F. *Thiamin and Ascorbic Acid Values of Raw and Canned Peas.* Food Research 12, 468-473, 1947.

2. Guerrant, N. B., Vavich, M. G., Fardig, O. B., Ellenberger, H. A., Stern, R. M., and Coonen, N. H. *Nutritive Value of Canned Foods. XXIII. Effect of Duration and Temperature of Blanch on Vitamin Retention by Certain Vegetables.* Ind. Eng. Chem. 39, 1000-1007, 1947.

3. Guerrant, N. B., Vavich, M. G., Fardig, O. B., Dutcher, R. A., and Stern, R. M. *The Nutritive Value of Canned Foods XX. Changes in the Vitamin Content of Foods During Canning.* J. Nutrition 32, 435-458, 1946.

4. Wagner, J. R., Strong, F. M. and Elvehjem, C. A. *Nutritive Value of Canned Foods. XIV. Effect of Commercial Canning Operation on the Ascorbic Acid, Thiamine, Riboflavin and Niacin Contents of Vegetables.* Ind. Eng. Chem. 39, 985-990, 1947.

5. Wagner, J. R., Strong, F. M. and Elvehjem, C. A. *Nutritive Value of Canned Foods. XV. Effects of Blanching on the Retention of Ascorbic Acid, Thiamine, and Niacin in Vegetables.* Ind. Eng. Chem. 39, 990-993, 1947.

6. Lamb, F. C., Pressley, A. and Zuch, T. *Nutritive Value of Canned Foods. XXI. Retention of Nutrients During Commercial Production of Various Canned Fruits and Vegetables.* Food Research 12, 273-287, 1947.

7. Cameron, E. J., Pilcher, R. W. and Clifcorn, L. E. *Nutrient Retention During Canned Food Production.* Am. J. Pub. Health 39, 756-763, 1949.

8. Pressley, A., Ridder, C., Smith, M. C. and Caldwell, E. *The Nutritive Value of Canned Foods. II. Ascorbic Acid and Carotene or Vitamin A Content.* J. Nutrition 28, 107-116, 1944.

9. Hinman, W. F., Higgins, M. M. and Halliday, E. G. *The Nutritive Value of Canned Foods. XVIII. Further Studies on Carotene, Ascorbic Acid and Thiamine.* J. Am. Dietet. Assoc. 23, 226-231, 1947.

10. Lamb, F. C., Lewis, L. D. and Lee, S. K. *Effect of Blanching on Retention of Ascorbic Acid and Thiamin in Peas.* Western Canner and Packer 40, No. 6, 60-62, 1948.

11. Feaster, J. F., Mudra, A. E., Ives, M. and Tompkins, M. D. *Effect of Blanching Time on Vitamin Retention in Canned Peas.* The Canner 108, No. 1, 27-30, 1949.

12. Heberlein, D. G., Ptak, L. R., Medoff, S. and Clifcorn, L. E. *Quality and Nutritive Value of Peas As Affected by Blanching.* Food Technology 4, 109-114, 1950.

13. *Relation of Genetic and Environmental Factors to the Vitamin Content of Fruit and Vegetables.* Nutrition Revs. 3, 216-219, 1945.

14. Ezell, B. D., Wilcox, M. S. and Hutchins, M. C. *Effect of Variety and Storage on Ascorbic Acid Content of the Sweet Potato.* Food Research **13**, 116-122, 1948.

15. Darrow, G. M., Wilcox, M. S., Scott, D. H. and Hutchins, M. C. *Breeding Strawberries for Vitamin C.* J. Heredity **38**, 363-365, 1947.

Chapter 5

CAROTENE AND VITAMIN A IN CANNED FOODS

Vitamin A is a fat-soluble factor essential for life and normal health. It has been found to be a complex organic compound, which can be grouped with the alcohols because of the presence of an hydroxyl group in the molecule; this group occurs in a side chain attached to a beta-ionone ring. Vitamin A itself as found in animal tissues, is colorless. Many plant tissues exhibit vitamin A activity and, in fact, the green leafy and the yellow vegetables are outstanding food sources of this essential in the human diet. In these foods, as well as in fruits, the vitamin A activity is due to the presence of an orange yellow pigment, which the body is able to convert into vitamin A. In the green, leafy vegetables, such as spinach, the yellow pigment is masked by the presence of chlorophyll. The yellow pigment has been shown to be one or more of a group of related compounds, called carotenes, because they first were isolated from carrots. There are three isomeric carotenes, alpha, beta, and gamma, which possess vitamin A activity. Beta-carotene is a hydrocarbon which contains two beta-ionone rings; theoretically it should be able to yield two molecules of vitamin A. The other isomeric carotenes contain only one of these rings and yield less vitamin A (1). Beta-carotene predominates in most vegetable foods. In corn, however, a related compound called cryptoxanthin, is present to a greater extent. It also possesses vitamin A activity.

The precise amounts of vitamin A which are derived from the different carotenes cannot be stated because utilization depends on a number of factors (2-4). For these reasons the actual value of a vegetable food as a source of vitamin A is somewhat less than would be indicated by laboratory examination for its content of carotene. However, in establishing standards of recommended allowances for vitamin A, the Food and Nutrition Board took into consideration the nature of the usual American diet, and established the allowances so that for all practical purposes fruits and vegetables may be considered to contribute to the vitamin A requirements of the body in accordance with their content of carotene, as determined by physico-chemical methods.

Vitamin A has been shown to function in the maintenance of the cells of the epithelial tissues. In its absence these cells become altered and subject to bacterial infection. Vitamin A is concerned with the visual purple of the retina of the eye; this property has been used in a method of measuring vitamin A requirements by the so-called dark adaptation tests. Recent studies suggest that characteristic alterations of the skin, and of the whites of the eyes, may be used in the medical appraisal of the status of vitamin A nutrition. These "little signs" of vitamin A deficiency are not seen in persons whose diet is completely adequate, and which includes liberal quantities of foods that supply vitamin A.

As has been stated, the green leafy and the yellow vegetables and certain fruits are notable sources of vitamin A-precursors, while liver, butterfat, egg yolk, and fish liver oils are excellent sources of the preformed vitamin A. Carrots, sweetpotatoes, spinach, and other leafy vegetables are outstanding sources. Apricots, purple plums (prunes), tomatoes, red cherries, green asparagus, peaches, and peas are good sources.

Carotene and Vitamin A Retentions During Canning

In the preservation of fruits and vegetables by canning the fat-soluble vitamins probably are the least affected of the vitamins by the various operations involved. Being essentially insoluble in water, these nutrients are not leached out of the solid foods during washing. When blanching of vegetables is done the loss of carotene is insignificant. The heating process is not as destructive as might otherwise be the case, because it is done in the absence of appreciable oxygen.

Cameron *et al.* (5) have summarized the results of work on over-all carotene retentions undertaken in the canned food nutrition program. These retentions are measured by analyses on the raw and on the final processed product. They picture the degree of conservation attained through the entire canning procedure. The results are shown graphically in Figure 10 which shows the percentage ranges and mean values of the products listed and, parenthetically, the numbers of observations made. The data show that canning procedures have only limited effect on carotene. Mean values ranged from 70 to 98 per cent retention. The low retention for

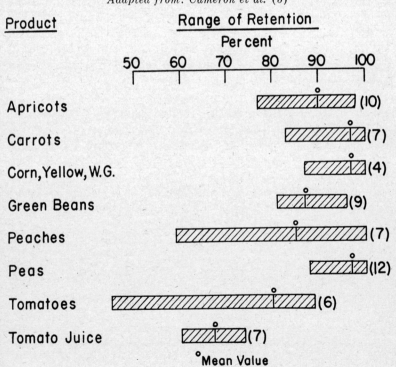

FIGURE 10.   Over-all Carotene Retentions

Adapted from: Cameron et al. (5)

FIGURE 11

Carotene Content of Canned Foods

Combined data from 1942 and 1943 Phase I surveys

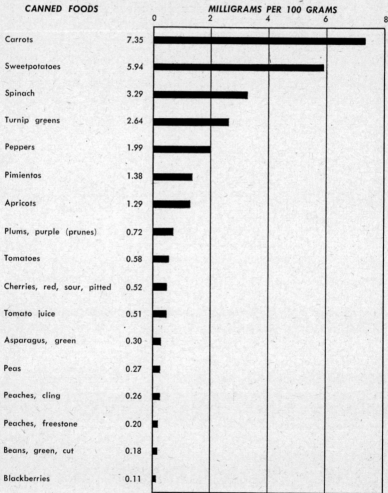

CANNED FOODS		MILLIGRAMS PER 100 GRAMS
Carrots	7.35	
Sweetpotatoes	5.94	
Spinach	3.29	
Turnip greens	2.64	
Peppers	1.99	
Pimientos	1.38	
Apricots	1.29	
Plums, purple (prunes)	0.72	
Tomatoes	0.58	
Cherries, red, sour, pitted	0.52	
Tomato juice	0.51	
Asparagus, green	0.30	
Peas	0.27	
Peaches, cling	0.26	
Peaches, freestone	0.20	
Beans, green, cut	0.18	
Blackberries	0.11	

NOTE: The following products, found to contain less than 0.10 mg. per 100 g., are not included above: White asparagus, baked beans, Lima beans, beets, blueberries, corn, grapefruit, kraut, mackerel, mushrooms, orange juice, pears, pineapple, salmon, sardines, shrimp, tuna.

tomato juice probably reflects the straining out of some carotene-containing material during extraction. The wide percentage range in the retention exhibited by tomatoes would appear to be due to variation in peeling and trimming of the tomatoes prior to filling into the can.

Carotene and Vitamin A Content of Canned Foods

Pressley *et al.* (6) and Hinman *et al.* (7) have reported the carotene or vitamin A contents of more than 40 canned foods. The data on carotene contents from these initial studies in the canned food nutrition program are to be found in Table III of the Appendix. A graphical interpretation of the data will be found in Figure 11. Vitamin A values on canned seafoods resulting from the studies by Pressley *et al.* are given, together with similar data from related studies, Neilands *et al.* (8), in Table V of the Appendix.

The results of the combined investigations on carotene have shown that among the canned foods, carrots, sweetpotatoes, spinach, and turnip greens are the best sources. Apricots, pimientos, purple plums, sweet peppers, tomatoes, tomato juice, and red cherries may be regarded as good sources. Among the fish products, mackerel, salmon, and sardines in oil are highest in vitamin A.

In contrast to the situation found in the case of water-soluble nutrients such as ascorbic acid, the B-vitamins and minerals, vitamin A and carotene are substantially retained in the solid portion of the product in the case of foods which are canned in a liquid packing medium. In the case of vitamin A of fish there may be some small decrease in the solid portion depending upon the extent to which the fish oil may enter the liquid packing medium.

Application to Human Nutrition

It has already been mentioned that in evaluating the relative importance of the products which supply carotene nonbiological assays may not provide a complete answer. There is evidence to show that the biological vitamin A activity of green vegetables is more closely related to the carotene content determined chemically than is the biological vitamin A activity of yellow and orange-colored vegetables. Graves (2) stated in a review article that the actual biological efficiency of yellow and orange-colored vegetables is only 21 to 25 per cent of the amount indicated by physical assay, while it is 70 to 100 per cent for green vegetables. For most dietary computations, however, all carotene present in a food or a diet may be considered to possess full vitamin A activity, because the dietary allowances have provided for differences in activity.

The carotene and vitamin A contributions as applied to practical problems in human nutrition are shown in Tables VI and VII of the Appendix. These Tables interpret the canned food values for carotene and vitamin A in terms of the proportions of Recommended Daily Allowances (National Research Council) and Minimum Daily Requirements (Food and Drug Administration) supplied by canned food servings. More than 40 canned foods were included. The Tables show that by proper selection of canned foods, carotene requirements may be met readily from even a limited number of products that would normally be included in well balanced diets. The carotene contents of products of lesser potency, however, will in the aggregate supply substantial contributions.

In Table X of the Appendix are tabulated nutritive values of canned food servings in terms of actual contents of nutrients and these values may be useful in the formulation of dietaries. In the case of fruits and vegetables the carotene contents have been expressed in terms of International Units of pro-vitamin A. One International (or U.S.P.) Unit of pro-vitamin A is the biological vitamin A activity of 0.6 microgram (0.0006 milligram) of beta-carotene.

Improvement of Initial Carotene Levels of Raw Food Materials

Suitability of a fruit or vegetable product for canning depends upon a number of factors such as: Adaptability to climate, disease resistance, growing habits, yield, form or shape, ease of handling in preparatory steps and the quality attainable in the canned product. Another factor to which the canning industry is devoting attention, is nutritive quality. Where a product is recognized as an inherently significant source of one or more vitamins it is expected that that product, raw or processed, will carry the nutritive value expected by the consumer. There is reason to assume, also, that where improvement is possible, attention will be given to its accomplishment.

Further research in plant genetics may result in increased carotene contents in vegetables and fruits that normally supply this vitamin. Through such research the carotene content of carrots for canning has been increased greatly, and similar research is being applied to sweetpotatoes and other vegetables (9-11).

REFERENCES

1. Association of Vitamin Chemists. *Methods of Vitamin Assay.* Interscience Publishers, Inc., N. Y., 47, 1947.

2. Graves, H. C. H. *The Vitamin A Value of Carotene in Vegetables.* Chem. and Ind. **61**, 8-10, 1942.

3. Fraps, G. S. and Meinke, W. W. *Digestibility by Rats of Alpha, Beta, and Neo-Beta-Carotenes in Vegetables.* Arch. Biochem. **6**, 323-327, 1945.

4. Callison, E. C., Orent-Keiles, E., Frenchman, R. and Zook, E. G. *Comparison of Chemical Analysis and Bioassay as Measures of Vitamin A Values of Some Vegetables and the Effect of Comminution upon the Bioassay Value.* J. Nutrition **37**, 139-152, 1949.

5. Cameron, E. J., Pilcher, R. W. and Clifcorn, L. E. *Nutrient Retention During Canned Food Production.* Am. J. Pub. Health **39**, 756-763, 1949.

6. Pressley, A., Ridder, C., Smith, M. C. and Caldwell, E. *The Nutritive Value of Canned Foods. II. Ascorbic Acid and Carotene or Vitamin A Content.* J. Nutrition **28**, 107-116, 1944.

7. Hinman, W. F., Higgins, M. M. and Halliday, E. G. *The Nutritive Value of Canned Foods. XVIII. Further Studies on Carotene, Ascorbic Acid, and Thiamine.* J. Am. Dietet. Assoc. **23**, 226-231, 1947.

8. Neilands, J. B., Strong, F. M. and Elvehjem, C. A. *The Nutritive Value of Canned Foods. XXV. Vitamin Content of Canned Fish Products.* J. Nutrition **34**, 633-643, 1947.

9. *Factors Influencing the Contents of Provitamin A and Vitamin C in Plants.* Nutrition Revs. 2, 271-274, 1944.

10. Kohler, G. W., Lincoln, R. E., Porter, J. W., Zscheile, F. P., Caldwell, R. M., Harper, R. H. and Silver, W. *Selection and Breeding for High Carotene Content (Provitamin A) in Tomato.* Botan. Gaz. 219-225, 1947.

11. *Improvement in Nutritive Value of Food by Plant Breeding Guided by Chemical Control.* Nutrition Revs. 7, 186-187, 1949.

Chapter 6

VITAMIN D IN CANNED FOODS

Vitamin D is a fat-soluble and water-insoluble vitamin that for a time was confused with vitamin A. The two vitamins occur together in cod liver oil and other fish liver oils. They were distinguished by the fact that the heating of the oil, while bubbling air through it, results in a complete destruction of the vitamin A activity, leaving the antirachitic potency unaffected. Vitamin D prevents or cures rickets in infants and children. It alters the metabolism of calcium and phosphorus, so that more calcium is absorbed, or less excreted, through the intestinal wall.

There now are known to be a number of substances which, after exposure to ultraviolet, have antirachitic potency (1). These substances belong to a group of organic compounds known as sterols. The principal sterols, which exhibit vitamin D potency after activation by ultraviolet, are ergosterol and 7-dehydrocholesterol. Ergosterol is obtained from yeast, and a purified, activated preparation of ergosterol is called calciferol. Activated ergosterol is sometimes called vitamin D_2. Activated 7-dehydrocholesterol is the vitamin D of fish liver oils and other animal sources. It is sometimes called vitamin D_3.

Exposure of the human body to sunlight results in the formation of vitamin D in the body. This is because of the action of the effective rays of the ultraviolet of sunlight on the vitamin D precursors in the skin. Irradiation of foods with ultraviolet results in the production of vitamin D from precursors in the food, and has been developed commercially. There are at least ten sterols which can be activated, either by irradiation with ultraviolet or by other special means.

Vitamin D is naturally present in only a few of the commonly eaten foods, such as the flesh of certain oil fish, fish roe and hen's eggs. However, a limited number of foods, such as milk and cereals, have been fortified with vitamin D and are commercially available.

Vitamin D is intimately associated with the metabolism of calcium and phosphorus. It is need for strong bones and good teeth, and should be provided for in the adequate feeding not only of infants but of growing children, adolescents, and pregnant and lactating women. It is also needed by adults and older persons, especially when exposure to sunlight is

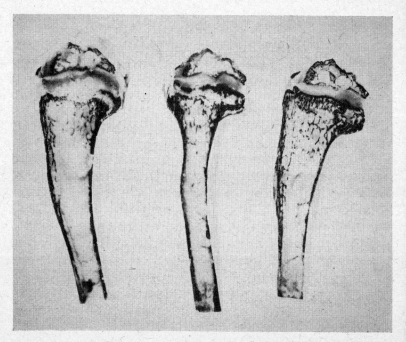

Courtesy American Can Company

Vitamin D is important in the metabolism of calcium and phosphorus in the body. It may be assayed in canned foods by measuring the effect on the bones of experimental animals. At left is a rachitic bone; center, a partially healed bone; and right, a completely healed bone.

limited. For adults who do not consume some controlled source of vitamin D, the few foods which do serve as significant sources of this factor assume added importance.

Vitamin D in Canned Fish

In the canned food nutrition studies (2) assays for vitamin D were performed according to the U.S.P. method on a number of canned fish products. The following foods were selected for this study: Mackerel, salmon, sardines, and tuna. As shown in Table V of the Appendix all samples of canned fish examined were found to be excellent sources of vitamin D. Canned salmon was found to be the outstanding source among the products examined.

No assays were made of vegetable and fruit products, because it is known that these, like most foods, contain little or no vitamin D. Because vitamin D is known to be extremely heat stable no retention studies were performed on the canned fish.

Application to Human Nutrition

Since 400 USP units of vitamin D represent both the recommended dietary allowance of the National Research Council and the minimum daily requirement of the Food and Drug Administration for food labeling purposes, the high vitamin D content found for the various species of fish are of great importance nutritionally. In the case of salmon, all the results obtained showed USP units per 100 grams in excess of the recommended daily allowance, and in the case of the other species, the amounts ranged from about 60 to 85 per cent.

Canned fortified evaporated milk which has not been included in this program is generally recognized as an important source of vitamin D, particularly for infants where canned milk is the chief ingredient of the formula.

REFERENCES

1. Rosenberg, H. R. *Chemistry and Physiology of the Vitamins.* Interscience Publishers, Inc., New York, 1942.
2. Neilands, J. B., Strong, F. M., and Elvehjem, C. A. *The Nutritive Value of Canned Foods XXV. Vitamin Content of Canned Fish Products.* J. Nutrition, 34, 633-643, 1947.

Chapter 7

THIAMINE IN CANNED FOODS

Thiamine, or vitamin B_1, is a member of the vitamin B complex. Its existence was indicated in 1911, the vitamin was isolated in 1926 and synthesized in 1936. At the present time hundreds of thousands of pounds of crystalline thiamine preparations are made each year, for the food enrichment programs, for animal feeds, and for therapeutic purposes. Thiamine is an organic compound which contains sulfur and nitrogen in the molecule. There are two ring structures, one a thiazole, which contains sulfur, and the other a pyrimidine, which contains nitrogen. Thiamine occurs in foods and tissues, largely as a pryophosphoric acid ester, called cocarboxylase. This compound is an enzyme which participates with others in cellular oxidations, and which is necessary to help the body to oxidize carbohydrates (1).

Insufficient thiamine in the diet is the major deficiency in the disease beriberi. Less severe deficiency of this vitamin in the diet may manifest itself by a number of signs and symtoms, including neuritis, nervousness, loss of appetite, alterations of the physiology of the gastro-intestinal tract, and inability to perform strenuous exercise.

Thiamine is easily soluble in water. In solution it is readily destroyed by heat in an alkaline medium.

Like ascorbic acid, thiamine is widely distributed in nature and is found in most foods of plant and animal origin. Unlike ascorbic acid, the amounts of thiamine found in the richest natural food sources of this factor are relatively small and seldom exceed 40 parts per million. There are a number of foods so high in ascorbic acid that average or convenient portions of these foods will supply all the daily

Courtesy American Can Company

Modern methods of measuring the nutritive quality of canned foods may involve many different special technics. A step in the microbiological determination of the B vitamins is illustrated.

requirement for this vitamin. This is not the case with thiamine. Furthermore, the human body is incapable of storing large quantities of this vitamin. For these reasons the securing of adequate daily amounts through natural foods is important. This circumstance was one of the considerations underlying the enrichment of certain foods with thiamine, along with other nutrients (2).

The best food sources of thiamine, because of their content of thiamine or the amounts or the frequency of their use in the diet, are the whole grain cereals; flour and bread which meet the standard requirements for enriched bread and flour; animal products such as meats, both muscle cuts and variety meats; poultry and fish; and certain vegetables, notably legumes.

Thiamine Retention During Canning

Because of its solubility in water and its sensitivity to heat, thiamine retention in raw foods during canning has been the subect of a number of investigations during the past 20 years. Most of the reports, however, were not based on commercial practices and the experimental procedures employed are subject to criticism. In some reports, the methods employed for vitamin estimation hardly permitted quantitative expression of the results obtained. The work of Clifcorn and Heberlein (3) on the effect of commercial canning on thiamine in vegetables supplied the most reliable information on this subject at the time of the inauguration of the canned food nutrition program which made possible further studies of this subject under controlled commercial and experimental conditions.

Retention During Blanching—Retention of thiamine in peas, asparagus, green beans, Lima beans, and spinach as a result of blanching was investigated by Wagner and associates (4), Guerrant *et al.* (5), and Lamb *et al.* (6). Results of these and related studies presented in a recent review (7) are summarized graphically in Figure 12.

FIGURE 12. Thiamine Retentions During Blanching

Adapted from: Cameron et al. (7)

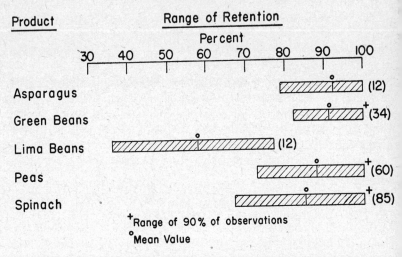

+Range of 90% of observations
°Mean Value

Referring to this figure, the mean thiamine retentions during blanching for asparagus, green beans, peas, and spinach varied from 85 per cent (spinach) to 92 per cent (asparagus), indicative of a high degree of thiamine retention in these products. Lima beans showed a mean thiamine retention of 58 per cent. These data suggest that despite the solubility of thiamine, commercial hot-water blanching procedures still permit retention of substantial amounts of this vitamin in common vegetables.

Retention During Heat Processing—Thiamine retention during heat processing received attention early in nutrition research on canned foods (8). As improved methods of vitamin assay were developed and reference standards for the vitamins became available more exact quantitative data on the effect of this operation were adduced (9). However, many of the reports available in the literature represented projection to commercial processing practice of data obtained in small scale experiments. Controlled tests on both commercial and experimental scales were, therefore, incorporated in the canned food nutrition program to obtain further and more exact information on this subject.

The severity of the heat treatment to which thiamine in canned food may be subjected during heat processing is determined by a number of factors (10). Those factors which are of significance in this connection are: The active acidity or pH of the food; the mechanism whereby heat is transferred through the food in the sealed container; and the size of the container in which the food is packed. The pH value of the food determines whether or not a processing temperature above that of boiling water is required.

The "low-acid" foods (pH 4.5 or above) are customarily processed under steam pressure at temperatures of 240° F. (116° C.) or higher (10). This group includes fish and marine products, meats, milk, and most of the common vegetables. The so-called "acid" foods (fruits, fruit products, tomatoes and related products, acidified or fermented foods) with pH values below 4.5 are usually processed at 212° F. (100° C.) or below.

The mechanism of heat transfer and the size of the container govern the time of the heat process required at any process temperature. A food heated by conduction alone requires a longer processing time than one heated by convection or by a combination of conduction and convection. Likewise, a product in a large container requires longer processing at the same temperature than does the identical product in a smaller can. From these considerations, it is obvious that the effect of heat processing on thiamine retention is chiefly of interest in the case of the low-acid foods because stability of this vitamin—especially in conduction-heating products of this class—is dependent both upon the time and temperature of the process, other conditioning factors (pH and can size) being equal (11).

In Table 11 are shown typical thiamine retentions in several canned foods reported by a number of investigators (3,

6, 12, 13, 14). While a loss during processing occurs, as would be expected, particularly in the low-acid canned foods, the retentions are surprisingly good in many instances.

TABLE 11

Thiamine Retention During Heat Processing

Adapted from: Clifcorn and Heberlein (3), Wagner et al. (12)
Guerrant et al. (13) and Lamb et al. (6, 14)

Canned Foods	Can Size	Clifcorn and Heberlein	Wagner et al.	Guerrant et al.	Lamb et al.
		Per Cent	Per Cent	Per Cent	Per Cent
Asparagus, green	No. 2	.....	69–89	.....	64–77
	No. 300	63–66	.....	.....	.....
Asparagus, white	No. 2	.....	.....	.....	72–85
Beans, green	No. 2	73–79	69–91	70	60–88
	No. 10	.....	92	67	61–92
Beans, Lima	No. 2	58–71	50–87	60	.....
Beans, wax	No. 2	.....	.....	67	.....
Carrots	No. 10	.....	.....	100	.....
Corn, whole grain	No. 2	.....	35–38	25	33–53
	307x306	.....	.....	25–50	.....
Peas	No. 2	59–69	59–77	56	50–83
	No. 10	.....	57–84	.....	46–66
Spinach	No. 10	.....	.....	33	.....
Tomatoes	No. 2	89	.....	.....	.....
	No. 10	.....	.....	100	.....
Tomato juice	No. 2	74	.....	82	88–100
	404x700	.....	.....	83–100	95–100

Over-all Retention—A considerable amount of work of the canned food nutrition program was devoted to over-all retention of thiamine during canning. The reports of Wagner *et al.* (12) Guerrant and associates (13), and Lamb *et al.* (6, 14) supply valuable detailed data on thiamine retention in the following canned foods:

Asparagus	Carrots	Spinach
Beans, green	Corn	Tomatoes
Beans, Lima	Peaches	Tomato juice
Beans, wax	Peas	

These studies were recently reviewed (7) and are summarized in Figure 13. To illustrate the general effects of canning on over-all retention, products such as asparagus, corn, green beans, Lima beans, peaches, peas, tomatoes, and tomato juice were chosen for presentation in this summary since in their preparation for canning these foods are subjected to diverse operations which may affect vitamin retention. As indicated by Figure 13, there is some variation in the extent of thiamine retention found for these products.

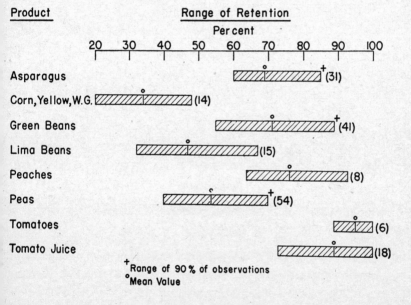

FIGURE 13. Over-all Thiamine Retentions

Adapted from: Cameron et al. (7)

The acid products (peaches, tomatoes, tomato juice) which do not require blanching and which are usually processed at 212° F. (100° C.) show high mean over-all thiamine retention (76 to 96 per cent). The low-acid foods (asparagus, corn, green beans, peas), subjected to blanching, to more severe

FIGURE 14

Thiamine Content of Canned Foods

Combined data from 1942 and 1943 Phase I surveys

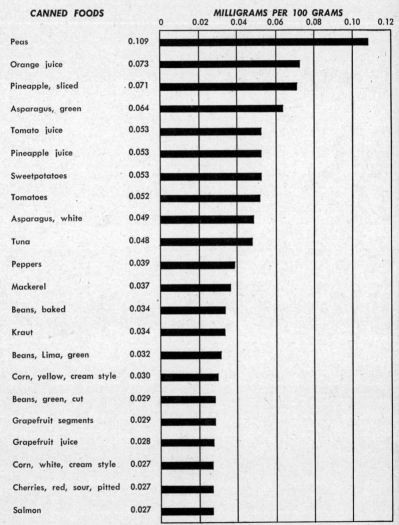

CANNED FOODS		MILLIGRAMS PER 100 GRAMS
Peas	0.109	
Orange juice	0.073	
Pineapple, sliced	0.071	
Asparagus, green	0.064	
Tomato juice	0.053	
Pineapple juice	0.053	
Sweetpotatoes	0.053	
Tomatoes	0.052	
Asparagus, white	0.049	
Tuna	0.048	
Peppers	0.039	
Mackerel	0.037	
Beans, baked	0.034	
Kraut	0.034	
Beans, Lima, green	0.032	
Corn, yellow, cream style	0.030	
Beans, green, cut	0.029	
Grapefruit segments	0.029	
Grapefruit juice	0.028	
Corn, white, cream style	0.027	
Cherries, red, sour, pitted	0.027	
Salmon	0.027	

FIGURE 14 (Continued)

Thiamine Content of Canned Foods

Combined data from 1942 and 1943 Phase I surveys

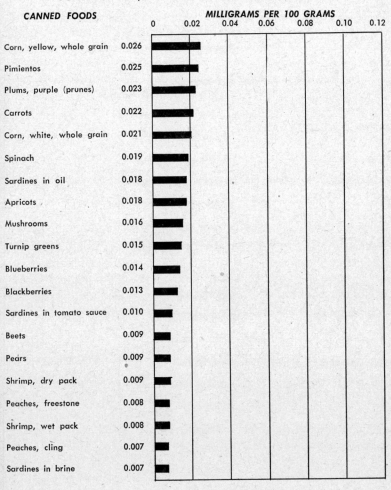

CANNED FOODS	MILLIGRAMS PER 100 GRAMS
Corn, yellow, whole grain	0.026
Pimientos	0.025
Plums, purple (prunes)	0.023
Carrots	0.022
Corn, white, whole grain	0.021
Spinach	0.019
Sardines in oil	0.018
Apricots	0.018
Mushrooms	0.016
Turnip greens	0.015
Blueberries	0.014
Blackberries	0.013
Sardines in tomato sauce	0.010
Beets	0.009
Pears	0.009
Shrimp, dry pack	0.009
Peaches, freestone	0.008
Shrimp, wet pack	0.008
Peaches, cling	0.007
Sardines in brine	0.007

heat processes, or to both, showed lower mean retentions (34 to 71 per cent).

Thiamine Content of Canned Foods

Table III of the Appendix lists the thiamine values of commercially canned foods as determined in studies sponsored in the nutrition program. For ready comparison, the average thiamine contents of the 41 canned foods reported in Table III of the Appendix have been presented graphically in Figure 14 in the order of thiamine content. The thiamine values are expressed on a 100 gram (3.5 ounce) basis, which is a convenient basis for computations. The data shown are based on the thiamine present in the entire contents of the cans, both liquids and solids.

Distribution Between Solid and Liquid Phases

Since thiamine, like ascorbic acid, is water-soluble and capable of extraction during home cooking and certain commercial food handling operations, studies were conducted to determine the distribution of thiamine between the solid and liquid phases of certain canned foods. In brief summary of these studies, it may be stated that most of the canned fruits studied contained about half of the thiamine in the liquid or syrup. In the canned vegetables about one-third of the total thiamine in the can contents was present in the liquid phase (15).

Application to Human Nutrition

To show the contributions which commercially canned foods may make to the daily diet, Table VI of the Appendix has been prepared. This table relates the thiamine contributions of the average servings of the canned foods listed to the recommended daily allowances suggested for this vitamin (Food and Nutrition Board, National Research Council) by showing the percentage of the daily allowances for thiamine supplied by these portions.

None of the vegetable, fruit, and fish products listed would be considered outstanding sources of thiamine in the raw, cooked, or canned forms, if considered only on the basis of the amount of thiamine per unit. However, the indicated servings of many of the canned foods listed supply from one to nine per cent of the recommended daily allowances for this vitamin. This contribution, small though it may be, supplements the thiamine contributions of the foods of cereal and animal origin commonly recognized as primary sources of this factor.

Future Improvements

With respect to future improvements in thiamine retentions in canned foods, new heat processing methods applicable to certain low-acid foods appear to hold great promise. These methods are of the "high-short" type (16) or involve reduction in process time by other principles (17). In either instance, significant improvements in thiamine retention have been found. It is likewise anticipated that alterations in existing commercial blanching schedules such as those found advantageous for ascorbic acid retention should also be effective in better retentions of thiamine. Also of interest, but as yet remote from commercial application, are entirely new blanching principles found experimentally to enhance thiamine retention (18, 19) in food. It is also possible that current research in plant genetics and agricultural practices may ultimately raise the natural initial thiamine content of field crops used for canning (20). These are subjects, possibly, for consideration in a Bulletin at some future date.

REFERENCES

1. Rosenberg, H. R. *Chemistry and Physiology of the Vitamins.* Interscience Publishers, Inc., New York, 1942.
2. *Nutritive Value of Enriched White Flour and Bread.* Nutrition Revs. 1, 295-297, 1943.
3. Clifcorn, L. E. and Heberlein, D. G. *Thiamine Content of Vegetables, Effect of Commercial Canning.* Ind. Eng. Chem. 36, 168-171, 1944.
4. Wagner, J. R., Strong, F. M., and Elvehjem, C. A. *Nutritive Value of Canned Foods. XV. Effects of Blanching on the Retention of Ascorbic Acid, Thiamine, and Niacin in Vegetables.* Ind. Eng. Chem. 39, 990-993, 1947.

5. Guerrant, N. B., Vavich, M. G., Fardig, O. B., Ellenberger, H. A., Stern, R. M. and Coonen, N. H. *Nutritive Value of Canned Foods. XXIII. Effect of Duration and Temperature of Blanch on Vitamin Retention by Certain Vegetables.* Ind. Eng. Chem. **39**, 1000-1007, 1947.

6. Lamb, F. C., Pressley, A. and Zuch, T. *Nutritive Value of Canned Foods. XXI. Retention of Nutrients During Commercial Production of Various Canned Fruits and Vegetables.* Food Research **12**, 273-287, 1947.

7. Cameron, E. J., Pilcher, R. W. and Clifcorn, L. E. *Nutrient Retention During Canned Food Production.* Am. J. Pub. Health **39**, 756-763, 1949.

8. Kohman, E. F. *Vitamins in Canned Foods.* National Canners Association Bull. 19-L (4th Rev.), 1937.

9. Feaster, J. F. and Alexander, O. R. *Planning Nutrition Studies Involving Canned Foods.* Ind. Eng. Chem. **36**, 172-176, 1944.

10. National Canners Association, Research Laboratory. *Processes for Low-Acid Canned Foods in Metal Containers.* Bull. 26-L (7th Ed.), 1950.

11. Feaster, J. F., Tompkins, M. D. and Ives, M. *Retention of Vitamins in Low-Acid Canned Foods.* Food Industries **20**, 14-17, 150, 152 and 154, 1949.

12. Wagner, J. R., Strong, F. M., and Elvehjem, C. A. *Nutritive Value of Canned Foods. XIV. Effect of Commercial Canning Operations on the Ascorbic Acid, Thiamine, Riboflavin, and Niacin Contents of Vegetables.* Ind. Eng. Chem. **39**, 985-990, 1947.

13. Guerrant, N. B., Vavich, M. G., Fardig, O. B., Dutcher, R. A. and Stern, R. M. *The Nutritive Value of Canned Foods. XX. Changes in the Vitamin Content of Foods During Canning.* J. Nutrition **32**, 435-458, 1946.

14. Lamb, F. C. (Unpublished data.)

15. Brush, M. K., Hinman, W. F. and Halliday, E. G. *The Nutritive Value of Canned Foods. V. Distribution of Water Soluble Vitamins Between Solid and Liquid Portions of Canned Vegetables and Fruits.* J. Nutrition **28**, 131-140, 1944.

16. Ball, C. O. *Advancement in Sterilization Methods for Canned Foods.* Food Research **3**, 13-55, 1938.

17. Roberts, H. L. and Sognefest, P. *Agitating Processes for Quality Improvement in Vacuum-Packed Vegetables.* The Canner **104**, No. 11, 20-24, 1947.

18. Moyer, J. C. and Stotz, E. *The Electronic Blanching of Vegetables.* Science **102**, 68-69, 1945.

19. Ives, M. *New Blanching Principles.* (Unpublished data.)

20. *Relation of Genetic and Environmental Factors to the Vitamin Content of Fruits and Vegetables.* Nutrition Revs. **3**, 216-219, 1945.

Chapter 8

RIBOFLAVIN IN CANNED FOODS

Riboflavin, or vitamin B_2, is a member of the vitamin B complex. Like other members of this group it is soluble in water and insoluble in fats. Unlike most of the other B vitamins, which are colorless in the pure form, crystalline riboflavin has a dark yellow color. The vitamin is present in such small concentrations in natural sources, that this color is not apparent. This property proved useful, together with another property—fluorescence when exposed to ultraviolet—when the initial attempts were made to isolate this factor (1).

The distinction between thiamine and riboflavin was first made clear as a result of heating rich natural sources, such as dried brewer's yeast, in an autoclave. Vitamin B_1 was destroyed by the excessive heating, leaving vitamin B_2 in large measure unaffected, and capable when suitably supplemented with other dietary essentials of promoting the growth of experimental animals.

Riboflavin has been characterized chemically as 6, 7-dimethyl-9-D-ribityl-isoalloxazine. It has a complex organic ring structure, isoal-loxazine, with three side chains, two of which are methyl groups, and the third, a five-carbon atom sugar, D-ribose. The vitamin now is produced commercially in considerable quantities each year. The crystals are slightly soluble in water, insoluble in fat solvents, relatively stable to heat, and destroyed by exposure to light, especially in an alkaline medium.

Riboflavin in the form of a phosphate functions as a component of a number of enzymes which are concerned with cellular oxidations. Apparently these enzymes are specially important in oxidations in the cornea of the eye, for in riboflavin deficiency this structure early shows pathologic changes.

143

There are a number of "little signs" of riboflavin deficiency which are important in the medical appraisal of nutritional status, and these are concerned with changes in the eye, skin and tongue. Experimental studies with animals repeatedly have shown a relationship between riboflavin and normal structure and function of the nervous system. Riboflavin is essential in the diet of human beings at all ages.

The principal dietary sources of this essential nutrient are milk, and milk products other than butter, meats, liver and other organ meats, fish, green leafy vegetables and legumes.

Riboflavin Retention During Canning

The property of relative heat stability would be expected to lead to good retention in canning, and investigations have verified this fact. Those unprocessed products which are normally good sources are good sources when canned. Where products are blanched a somewhat lower retention may be expected, owing to solubility in the blanch water. The extent of solution depends upon a number of factors, such as time and temperature of blanching, area of surface exposed, and the nature and maturity of the product.

Cameron et al. (2) have reported on nutrient retentions in canning, including "over-all" and "step-by-step" retentions. The former measures percentage-wise the nutrient differences between the raw and the final canned product, while the latter measures the effects of the different stages in preparation, and the heating processes. In the main, these losses of riboflavin which take place during canning occur chiefly during the blanching procedure.

"Over-all" retentions for riboflavin are charted in Figure 16. These values would be considered excellent both from the standpoint or range and of the indicated mean retentions, the latter of which exceed 80 per cent.

Retentions during the blanching operations are shown in Figure 15. The water solubility of riboflavin, along with other B-vitamins, leads to some loss through leaching during the blanching period. Green beans showed highest mean retention (95 per cent) with asparagus next in order (90 per cent). The lowest mean retention was noted for peas (75 per cent). The spreads in retention values, notably in the case of Lima beans (60-100 per cent), reflect the effect of different blanching procedures. In these procedures various combinations of time and temperature were used with variable effects; there was also some variation in maturity of the beans which were selected for canning.

FIGURE 15. Riboflavin Retentions During Blanching

Adapted from: Cameron et al. (2)

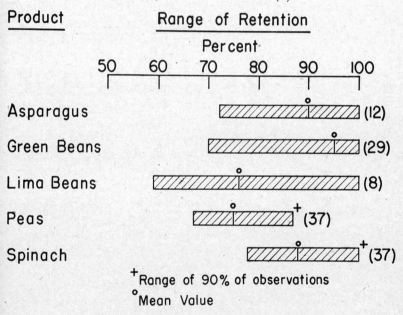

The properties of riboflavin indicate the measures for its preservation in the handling of products from harvest through the canning operations. In the case of vegetables and fruits there is no suggestion of destructive oxidative or enzymatic effects that take place where some other vitamins, such as ascorbic acid, are involved. The suggestions that have been made in regard to handling of products so as to afford greatest protection to ascorbic acid apply generally for the protection of riboflavin, as well as other vitamins.

FIGURE 16. Over-all Riboflavin Retentions

Adapted from: Cameron et al. (2)

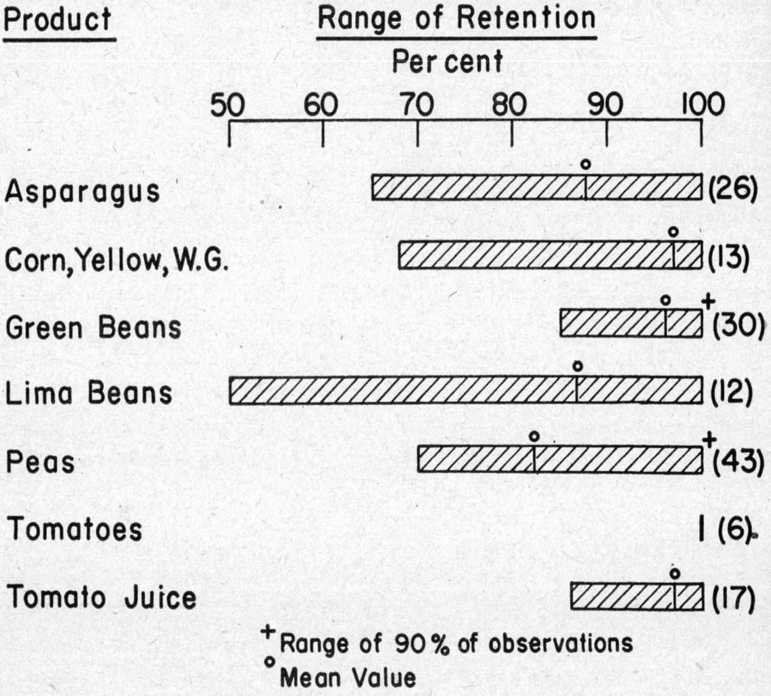

| Product | Range of Retention |

+ Range of 90% of observations
° Mean Value

Riboflavin Content of Canned Foods

Riboflavin is to be found in useful amounts in a wide range of canned foods produced in large quantities by the canning industry. In Table III of the Appendix, values for riboflavin are listed for 41 canned products which were assayed by various investigators as part of the canned food nutrition program (3-5). Riboflavin contents are expressed in terms of milligrams per 100 grams of product. Maximum, minimum, and average amounts are shown. The analyses upon which these figures were based were made upon the total contents of each can including liquid, except where indicated.

The average values which have been given in tabular form are presented graphically in Figure 17. For ready reference the products are listed in the descending order of riboflavin potencies. As in Table III, the results are given on a 100 gram basis (3.5 ounces). This chart shows at a glance that of the canned foods which were tested, certain canned fish products are superior in riboflavin content. Mushrooms are high in the list, and green vegetables top the vegetable group.

Distribution Between Solid and Liquid Phases

Brush *et al.* (6) have shown that in contrast to other water-soluble vitamins, concentrations of riboflavin are consistently higher in the solid than in the liquid portion of canned foods. Values range from 70 to 80 per cent in the solid, with 30 to 20 per cent in the liquid portions of eight vegetables in consumer size cans. Essentially similar results were obtained in No. 10 cans, except in the case of spinach, where the heating process requires a relatively lower "fill-in" weight and a correspondingly higher amount of brine. Here the solid portion contained 60 per cent of the riboflavin. Seven fruits in consumer sizes contained from 53 to 69 per cent in the solid fruit material.

Although these values show greater retentions in the solid material there is, nevertheless, a valuable content in the liquid, emphasizing again the general advice that liquid portion of canned foods could well be utilized.

Application to Human Nutrition

The expression of riboflavin contents of canned foods in terms of the recommended daily allowances of the National

FIGURE 17

Riboflavin Content of Canned Foods

Combined data from 1942 and 1943 Phase I surveys

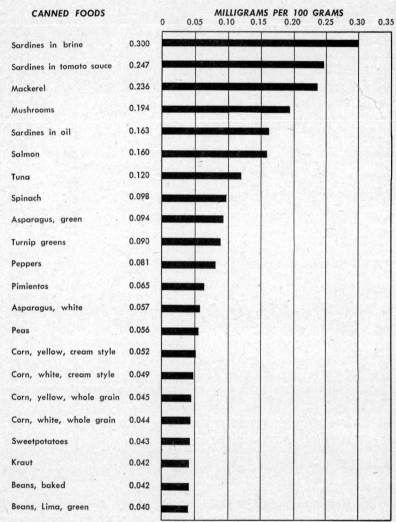

CANNED FOODS	MILLIGRAMS PER 100 GRAMS
Sardines in brine	0.300
Sardines in tomato sauce	0.247
Mackerel	0.236
Mushrooms	0.194
Sardines in oil	0.163
Salmon	0.160
Tuna	0.120
Spinach	0.098
Asparagus, green	0.094
Turnip greens	0.090
Peppers	0.081
Pimientos	0.065
Asparagus, white	0.057
Peas	0.056
Corn, yellow, cream style	0.052
Corn, white, cream style	0.049
Corn, yellow, whole grain	0.045
Corn, white, whole grain	0.044
Sweetpotatoes	0.043
Kraut	0.042
Beans, baked	0.042
Beans, Lima, green	0.040

FIGURE 17 (Continued)

Riboflavin Content of Canned Foods

Combined data from 1942 and 1943 Phase I surveys

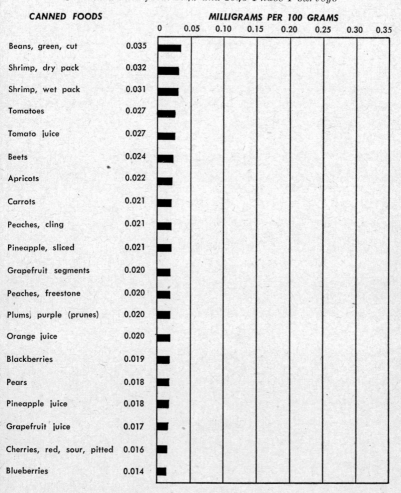

CANNED FOODS	MILLIGRAMS PER 100 GRAMS
Beans, green, cut	0.035
Shrimp, dry pack	0.032
Shrimp, wet pack	0.031
Tomatoes	0.027
Tomato juice	0.027
Beets	0.024
Apricots	0.022
Carrots	0.021
Peaches, cling	0.021
Pineapple, sliced	0.021
Grapefruit segments	0.020
Peaches, freestone	0.020
Plums, purple (prunes)	0.020
Orange juice	0.020
Blackberries	0.019
Pears	0.018
Pineapple juice	0.018
Grapefruit juice	0.017
Cherries, red, sour, pitted	0.016
Blueberries	0.014

Research Council and the minimum daily requirements of the Food and Drug Administration will be found in Table VI and Table VII of the Appendix. These Tables show the respective proportions of the daily allowances and minimum requirements supplied by canned food servings. The servings are for the individual products in terms of weights and measures which were determined experimentally by the Home Economic Division of the National Canners Association.

These tables show strikingly the importance of certain canned fish products which present the greatest contributions on a serving basis. Thus, sardines in tomato sauce (Pilchards) with a 106-gram serving would provide 15 per cent of the recommended daily allowance. Mackerel, with the same size serving, would provide 12 per cent. Salmon, with a 113-gram serving, gives 10 per cent, and 102 grams of spinach, 8 per cent. A serving of 90 grams of canned mushrooms provides 10 per cent of the recommended allowance for riboflavin.

The tables to which reference has been made show a general occurrence of riboflavin in canned foods, but relatively few products that are outstanding sources. In this respect, riboflavin is like thiamine. As in the case of thiamine, also, each food assumes significance as a contributor to the total dietary intake of riboflavin, while emphasis in meal planning must be placed on the few outstanding food sources.

Riboflavin values of canned food servings are listed in Table X of the Appendix in terms of actual content in milligrams. This Table should prove useful in the computation of diets.

REFERENCES

1. Rosenberg, H. R. *Chemistry and Physiology of the Vitamins.* Interscience Publishers, Inc., New York, 1942.
2. Cameron, E. J., Pilcher, R. W. and Clifcorn, L. E. *Nutrient Retention During Canned Food Production.* Am. J. Pub. Health **39**, 756-763, 1949.
3. Thompson, M. L., Cunningham, E. and Snell, E. E. *The Nutritive Value of Canned Foods. IV. Riboflavin and Pantothenic Acid.* J. Nutrition **28**, 123-129, 1944.

4. Ives, M., Zepplin, M., Ames, S. R., Strong, F. M. and Elvehjem, C. A. *The Nutritive Value of Canned Foods. X. Further Studies on Riboflavin, Niacin, and Pantothenic Acid.* J. Amer. Dietet. Assoc. **21,** 357-359, 1949.

5. Neilands, J. B., Strong, F. M. and Elvehjem, C. A. *The Nutritive Value of Canned Foods. XXV. Vitamin Content of Canned Fish Products.* J. Nutrition **34,** 633-643, 1947.

6. Brush, M. K., Hinman, W. F. and Halliday, E. G. *The Nutritive Value of Canned Foods. V. Distribution of Water Soluble Vitamins Between Solid and Liquid Portions of Canned Vegetables and Fruits.* J. Nutrition **28,** 131-140, 1944.

Chapter 9

NIACIN IN CANNED FOODS

Niacin is the name given to nicotinic acid, or 3-pyridine carboxylic acid, an important member of the vitamin B complex which is involved in the prevention of the deficiency disease, pellagra. It occurs in foods chiefly in the form of the amide, niacinamide (1).

The discovery of the importance of niacin in the treatment of pellagra arose primarily from two lines of investigations. The first was the demonstration that the condition called blacktongue in dogs was the analogue of pellagra in man. This provided an experimental animal for controlled studies in nutrition. The second line of investigations was the demonstration that fractions of liver extract were potent in the prevention or cure of blacktongue in dogs, which led to the isolation of niacinamide as the effective substance in liver. Successful trials of the value of niacin, or its amide, in the treatment of pellagra soon followed.

It was recognized, however, that in both the human and the canine diseases other factors were important, and that the diseases were multiple deficiency conditions. Other members of the vitamin B complex were found to be involved, and also the tryptophan content of the diet. Studies with laboratory rats showed that this amino acid could serve as a precursor of niacin in the body, that is, that out of the tryptophan the body could chemically make niacin.

Niacinamide functions as a component of the two complex substances which are important in cellular oxidations. These substances were Coenzyme I and Coenzyme II, and they are concerned with the oxidation of carbohydrate derivatives.

The vitamin is stable to heat and light and is not affected by the cooking of foods. It is found chiefly in liver, meats, fish and poultry, and in whole wheat products, but vegetable and fruit products are of secondary importance. The effectiveness of milk in the dietary management of pellagra is probably due to the high content of tryptophan in its proteins. Niacin is soluble in hot water, but to a lesser degree than niacinamide (2).

Niacin Retentions During Canning

"Step-by-step" retentions of niacin have been determined for asparagus, yellow whole grain corn, green beans, Lima beans and peas (3-5). These retentions, as contrasted to "over-all" retentions, show the effect of each preparatory operation as well as the final heating process. Green beans and Lima beans, which in preparation for canning are blanched, suffered some loss as a result of this treatment—retentions ranging from 60 to 100 per cent. The whole grain corn exhibited high retentions through the various preparation steps. Values for "over-all" retentions (raw vs. finished canned products) were 77 to 100 per cent. In all cases, due to the heat stability of niacin, process temperature effects were small.

It has been reported by Cameron *et al.* (6) that for most of the products listed the canning procedures involved have small "over-all" effect on niacin. Figure 18, which summarizes the data in graphic form, shows that the lowest mean niacin retention, that observed for peas, was about 65 per cent. For the remaining products the mean niacin retentions were more than 80 per cent. Values higher than 90 per cent were noted for half the number of products listed. The wide range of retentions indicated for canned peas may be ascribed in part at least, to the degree of maturity and to variation in blanching treatments.

Figure 19 provides in graphic form the combined results of blanching studies on five vegetables. Despite the solubility of niacin there is an indication from these data that blanching retentions are higher for niacin than is the case with certain other members of the water-soluble vitamins such as ascorbic acid (page 107) and thiamine (page 131). For all except one product, the retentions were greater than 80 per cent, and with two products (asparagus and green beans) more than 90 per cent. The lowest mean value was found for peas, and this was in excess of 70 per cent. These results would suggest that niacin is more firmly bound in vegetable products than is the case with other members of the water-soluble group.

FIGURE 18. Over-all Niacin Retentions

Adapted from: Cameron et al. (6)

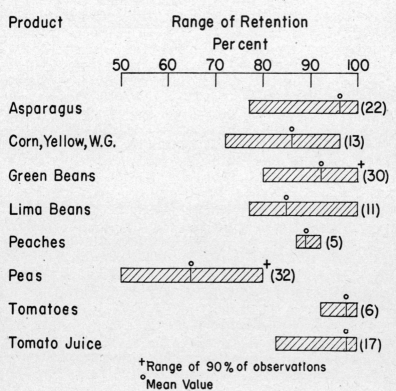

+Range of 90% of observations

°Mean Value

The generally high retentions that have been observed in the case of niacin may be associated with its stability during preparation treatments and in the sterilization process. Somewhat greater retentions may be obtained through modification in the blanching method. Special studies on blanching (7, 8) have shown that, as a general principle, high-temperature short-time blanching results in less depletion of the water-soluble vitamins, including niacin, than is the case when low-temperature long-time blanching is employed.

FIGURE 19. Niacin Retentions during Blanching

Adapted from: Cameron et al. (6)

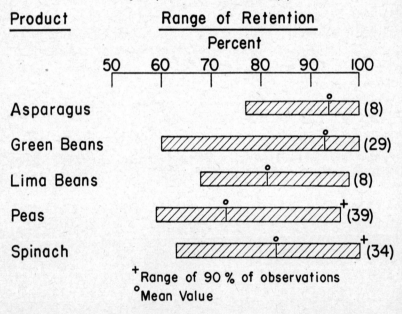

Niacin Content of Canned Foods

Among the products included in the vitamin studies of the canned foods nutrition program the canned fish products were outstanding in niacin content (9-11). Canned meat and poultry products were not included in these studies but are similarly recognized as excellent sources (12, 13). The niacin contents of canned vegetables and fruits were nearly equal to the values for these products in the raw state, and many of the values represent significant contributions toward the human requirement.

In Table III of the Appendix are listed the niacin contents of commercially canned foods as determined in the canned foods nutrition program (9-11). The findings are portrayed graphically in Figure 20 in which the contents are shown for the respective products in the order of descending potencies.

Application to Human Nutrition

Table X of the Appendix presents a practical concept of the niacin contributions which are afforded by 41 canned foods. Amounts of niacin are given on a "per serving" basis, the servings having been determined experimentally by the Home Economics Division of the National Canners Association. This Table may be useful in the formulation of diets.

Tables VI and VII present similar data in terms of proportions of recommended daily allowances (National Research Council) and minimum daily requirements (Food and Drug Administration). Both tables show dramatically the outstanding niacin values offered by the fish products. For example, a 100-gram (3.5 ounces) serving of tuna will supply nearly 70 per cent of the recommended daily allowance, or 100 per cent of the minimum daily requirement.

It will be seen also that the niacin contributions of the vegetables and fruits are not insignificant although substantially below those of canned fish. Canned mushrooms with a 90-gram serving will supply 10 per cent of the recommended daily allowance, or 14 per cent of the minimum daily requirement. Servings of peas, corn, baked beans, and asparagus provide more than five per cent of the recommended daily allowance.

FIGURE 20

Niacin Content of Canned Foods

Combined data from 1942 and 1943 Phase I surveys

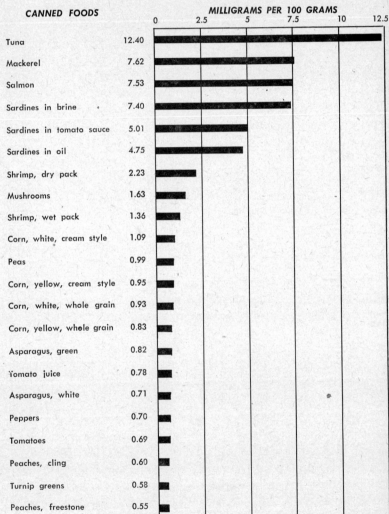

CANNED FOODS	
Tuna	12.40
Mackerel	7.62
Salmon	7.53
Sardines in brine	7.40
Sardines in tomato sauce	5.01
Sardines in oil	4.75
Shrimp, dry pack	2.23
Mushrooms	1.63
Shrimp, wet pack	1.36
Corn, white, cream style	1.09
Peas	0.99
Corn, yellow, cream style	0.95
Corn, white, whole grain	0.93
Corn, yellow, whole grain	0.83
Asparagus, green	0.82
Tomato juice	0.78
Asparagus, white	0.71
Peppers	0.70
Tomatoes	0.69
Peaches, cling	0.60
Turnip greens	0.58
Peaches, freestone	0.55

MILLIGRAMS PER 100 GRAMS (0, 2.5, 5, 7.5, 10, 12.5)

FIGURE 20 (Continued)

Niacin Content of Canned Foods

Combined data from 1942 and 1943 Phase I surveys

CANNED FOODS		MILLIGRAMS PER 100 GRAMS					
		0	2.5	5	7.5	10	12.5
Beans, Lima, green	0.54						
Beans, baked	0.51						
Sweetpotatoes	0.49						
Pimientos	0.38						
Plums, purple (prunes)	0.36						
Carrots	0.35						
Apricots	0.35						
Spinach	0.32						
Beans, green, cut	0.32						
Orange juice	0.24						
Blackberries	0.21						
Grapefruit segments	0.21						
Blueberries	0.19						
Cherries, red, sour, pitted	0.19						
Pineapple juice	0.18						
Grapefruit juice	0.17						
Pineapple, sliced	0.17						
Pears	0.14						
Beets	0.14						
Kraut	0.11						

REFERENCES

1. Rosenberg, H. R. *Chemistry and Physiology of the Vitamins.* Interscience Publishers, Inc., New York, 1942.

2. Russell, W. C., Taylor, M. W. and Beuk, J. S. *Nicotinic Acid Content of Common Fruits and Vegetables as Prepared for Human Consumption.* J. Nutrition **25**, 275-284, 1943.

3. Wagner, J. R., Strong, F. M. and Elvehjem, C. A. *Nutritive Value of Canned Foods. XIV. Effect of Commercial Canning Operations on the Ascorbic Acid, Thiamine, Riboflavin, and Niacin Contents of Vegetables.* Ind. Eng. Chem. **39**, 985-990, 1947.

4. Guerrant, N. B., Vavich, M. G., Fardig, O. B., Dutcher, R. A. and Stern, R. M. *The Nutritive Value of Canned Foods. XX. Changes in the Vitamin Content of Foods During Canning.* J. Nutrition **32**, 435-458, 1946.

5. Lamb, F. C., Pressley, A. and Zuch, T. *Nutritive Value of Canned Foods. XXI. Retention of Nutrients During Commercial Production of Various Canned Fruits and Vegetables.* Food Research **12**, 273-287, 1947.

6. Cameron, E. J., Pilcher, R. W. and Clifcorn, L. E. *Nutrient Retention During Canned Food Production.* Am. J. Pub. Health **39**, 756-763, 1949.

7. Wagner, J. R., Strong, F. M. and Elvehjem, C. A. *Nutritive Value of Canned Foods. XV. Effects of Blanching on the Retention of Ascorbic Acid, Thiamine, and Niacin in Vegetables.* Ind. Eng. Chem. **39**, 990-993, 1947.

8. Guerrant, N. B., Vavich, M. G., Fardig, O. B., Ellenberger, H. A., Stern, R. M. and Coonen, N. H. *Nutritive Value of Canned Foods. XXIII. Effect of Duration and Temperature of Blanch on Vitamin Retention by Certain Vegetables.* Ind. Eng. Chem. **39**, 1000-1007, 1947.

9. Ives, M., Wagner, J. R., Elvehjem, C. A. and Strong, F. M. *The Nutritive Value of Canned Foods. III. Thiamine and Niacin.* J. Nutrition **28**, 117-121, 1944.

10. Ives, M., Zepplin, M., Ames, S. R., Strong, F. M. and Elvehjem, C. A. *The Nutritive Value of Canned Foods. X. Further Studies on Riboflavin, Niacin, and Pantothenic Acid.* J. Am. Dietet. Assoc. **21**, 357-359, 1945.

11. Neilands, J. B., Strong, F. M. and Elvehjem, C. A. *The Nutritive Value of Canned Foods. XXV. Vitamin Content of Canned Fish Products.* J. Nutrition **34**, 633-643, 1947.

12. Greenwood, D. A., Kraybill, H. R., Feaster, J. F. and Jackson, J. M. *Vitamin Retention in Processed Meat. Effect of Thermal Processing.* Ind. Eng. Chem. **36**, 922-927, 1944.

13. Boyd, E. F., Eads, M. G. and Sandstead, H. R. *Food Value Tables for Calculation of Diet Records.* Fed. Security Agency, U. S. Pub. Health Service, Washington, D. C., Jan. 1947.

Chapter 10

OTHER B VITAMINS IN CANNED FOODS

Probably in no other field of nutrition research have more advances been made in recent years than in the study of the components of the vitamin B complex, their relation to the processes of living cells, and their significance in human nutrition. The following substances are now known to be important: Pantothenic acid, biotin, folic acid, pyridoxine, choline and vitamin B_{12}. All of these are water-soluble factors. Inositol and para-amino benzoic acid are also members of the vitamin B complex. There are still other factors which have been reported and, in addition, it is highly probable that hitherto unrecognized vitamins in this general group of water-soluble factors will become evident as investigations proceed.

For none of these factors has any standard for their probable human requirement been formulated. Several of these factors are known to be of undoubted significance in human as well as in animal nutrition. They are found in natural foods. It is considered that a well-rounded diet which is adequate in other respects probably supplies a sufficient amount of these other vitamins which only recently have become recognized.

Pantothenic acid—Pantothenic acid is a derivative of beta-alanine. It is an oil, readily soluble in water, which forms salts; the calcium salt is a crystalline solid which is commercially produced. This vitamin functions as a component of coenzyme A and is concerned with the metabolism of carbohydrates and fats. A wealth of experimental evidence with animals attests the importance of this factor to good nutritive condition. Best sources among foods include organ meats, dried and fresh legumes, fish and poultry. Pantothenic acid is stable to heat in the presence of moisture.

Biotin—Biotin is a complex organic compound, containing sulfur, which has been isolated and synthesized. It apparently is concerned with both fat and carbohydrate metabolism in the cells. Experimental studies have reported abnormalities of the skin, nervous system and muscles of animals, and probably of man, when restricted to diets specially low in this factor. An aid in producing the deficiency experimentally is the property that biotin exhibits of combining with avidin, a protein of raw egg white, to form a stable complex that is nutritionally unavailable to the body. Heating breaks down the complex and renders the biotin available. Among the best food sources of this vitamin are dried legumes and beef liver.

Pyridoxine—Pyridoxine, or vitamin B_6, is a derivative of pyradine with two primary alcohol side-chains. Pyridoxal is the name of the compound with one of these alcohol groups converted to an aldehyde. This is the biologically effective material into which pyridoxine, and its amine, pyridoxamine, are converted in the body.

Pyridoxal phosphate is a coenzyme involved in amino acid metabolism and probably with the metabolism of other foodstuffs. Animals restricted to a diet lacking in pyridoxine show abnormalities of the skin and nervous system, and a microcytic, hypochromic anemia (the red blood cells are markedly reduced in number, smaller in size, and contain less hemoglobin per cell). The vitamin is relatively heat stable. Among the best sources are liver, dried legumes, wheat germ, cabbage and sweetpotatoes.

Folic acid—Folic acid is the name given to a group of factors which have been variously designated in the course of experimental work which led to their isolation. Chemically the compounds are pteroylglutamic acids which have been obtained as bright yellow crystals. The manner in which folic acid functions in the body is still under active investigation. Folic acid is vitally concerned with the mechanism of blood formation in the bone marrow. A deficiency results in a macrocytic, hyperchromic type of anemia (which is characterized by the occurrence of a smaller number of large sized red blood cells, containing more than the usual amount of hemoglobin per cell). The anemia observed in many cases of pellagra is relieved by the administration of folic acid, which is further indication of the multiple nature of the factors responsible for this deficiency disease. The macrocytic anemias of sprue and of pernicious anemia are also alleviated by folic acid, but the changes in the nervous system observed in pernicious anemia are not affected except by administration of still another factor, vitamin B_{12}. Good dietary sources of folic acid include the green leafy vegetables, green asparagus, mushrooms, liver, meats and poultry, oysters, legumes, and whole wheat. The vitamin is readily inactivated by heat in an acid medium, less affected in a less acid or neutral medium, and it is destroyed by exposure to light.

Other Factors—Choline is still another substance which may be included among the water-soluble vitamins. Chemically, it is a quaternary ammonium compound characterized as hydroxyethyltrimethyl ammonium hydroxide. It occurs in the body combined as phospholipids, or acetylcholine, compounds which were known before the nutritional signficance of choline had been reported. The requirements are high, compared to the weights of some of the other essential vitamins, because choline serves as a source material of labile methyl groups, which in turn are involved in appreciable amounts in protein metabolism. Deficiency of choline leads to the production of fatty livers, and abnormalities in both liver and kidney function. Choline is essential for normal growth and general well-being. Among the good dietary sources are egg yolk, liver and organ meats, legumes, spinach, and the germs of cereal grains.

Para-amino benzoic acid is another water-soluble factor which has been studied. It is found as a part of the folic acid molecule.

Vitamin B_{12} only recently has become characterized (1948). The molecule contains cobalt. The vitamin is needed in very

FIGURE 21

Calcium Pantothenate Content of Canned Foods.

Combined data from 1942 and 1943 Phase I surveys

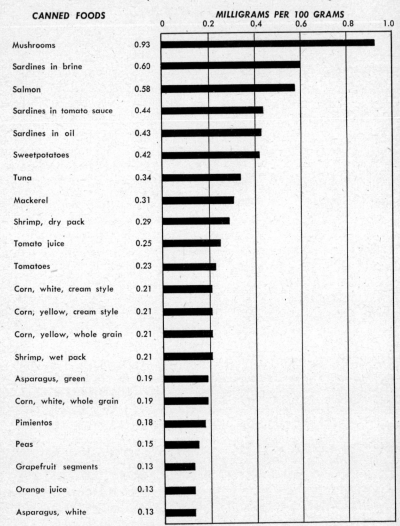

CANNED FOODS	
Mushrooms	0.93
Sardines in brine	0.60
Salmon	0.58
Sardines in tomato sauce	0.44
Sardines in oil	0.43
Sweetpotatoes	0.42
Tuna	0.34
Mackerel	0.31
Shrimp, dry pack	0.29
Tomato juice	0.25
Tomatoes	0.23
Corn, white, cream style	0.21
Corn, yellow, cream style	0.21
Corn, yellow, whole grain	0.21
Shrimp, wet pack	0.21
Asparagus, green	0.19
Corn, white, whole grain	0.19
Pimientos	0.18
Peas	0.15
Grapefruit segments	0.13
Orange juice	0.13
Asparagus, white	0.13

MILLIGRAMS PER 100 GRAMS
0   0.2   0.4   0.6   0.8   1.0

FIGURE 21 (Continued)

Calcium Pantothenate Content of Canned Foods

Combined data from 1942 and 1943 Phase I surveys

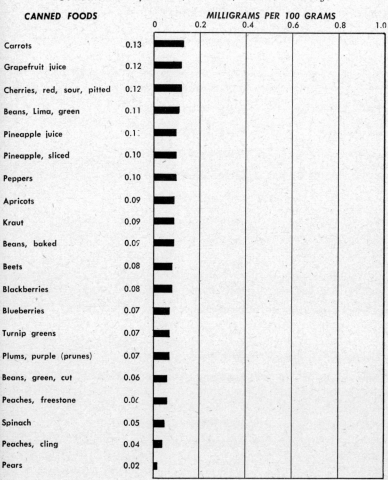

CANNED FOODS	MILLIGRAMS PER 100 GRAMS
Carrots	0.13
Grapefruit juice	0.12
Cherries, red, sour, pitted	0.12
Beans, Lima, green	0.11
Pineapple juice	0.1
Pineapple, sliced	0.10
Peppers	0.10
Apricots	0.09
Kraut	0.09
Beans, baked	0.09
Beets	0.08
Blackberries	0.08
Blueberries	0.07
Turnip greens	0.07
Plums, purple (prunes)	0.07
Beans, green, cut	0.06
Peaches, freestone	0.06
Spinach	0.05
Peaches, cling	0.04
Pears	0.02

small quantities, almost unbelievably small. This vitamin is the long sought substance in liver which is capable of relieving pernicious anemia. It is, therefore, inter-related in its functions with those of folic acid and other factors.

Canned Foods as Sources of the Lesser Known B Vitamins

After studies of the better known vitamins, for which dietary allowances had been established, were well under way in the canned food nutrition program, it was decided to conduct a survey of canned foods to determine the content of some of the newer factors of the vitamin B complex. Samples of known history were collected and assayed for pantothenic acid, biotin, folic acid and pyridoxine.

The pantothenic acid contents of 40 different canned foods as reported by Thompson *et al.* (1), Ives *et al.* (2) and Neilands *et al.* (3) are summarized in Table III of the Appendix. The average values are shown graphically in Figure 21. In the figure the products are shown in descending order of potency. It will be seen that the majority of fish products and mushrooms are the best sources of this vitamin. Several of the vegetables, namely, sweetpotatoes, tomato juice, tomatoes, white corn, yellow corn, and green asparagus also showed a substantial pantothenic acid content.

At the time the pantothenic acid studies were made, an enzymic digestion procedure was employed to liberate the vitamin. Since that time improved procedures have been developed, which give somewhat higher values. For this reason the data for the pantothenic acid content of canned foods may be regarded as minimum values.

The following 13 canned foods were assayed for biotin, folic acid, and pyridoxine: Green asparagus, green beans, carrots, yellow corn, grapefruit juice, mackerel, peaches, peas, salmon, sardines, spinach, tomatoes, and tuna (4). The results are presented in Table IV of the Appendix. The percentage distribution of these vitamins between the solids and the liquid of the can was also determined on the fruits and vegetables, and the results are shown in Table 12.

TABLE 12

Distribution of Pyridoxine, Biotin and Folic Acid in Canned Foods

Adapted from: Ives et al. (3)

Canned Foods	Pyridoxine	Biotin	S. Lactis Factor	L. Casei Factor [1]
	Percent of total present in the solids [2]			
Asparagus, green [3]	65	91	68	65
Beans, green	63	85	67	64
Carrots	66	77	74	72
Corn, yellow	72	88	77	73
Peaches	67	89	80	78
Peas	64	88	83	66
Spinach	64	99	67	63
Tomatoes	66	68	63	66

[1]Now demonstrated to be folic acid.

[2]Average values for 5 different samples of each product obtained by separate analysis of the liquids and drained solids. The difference between the figures given and 100 represents the percentage found to be present in the liquid in each instance.

[3]Six samples analyzed.

The fish products contained the largest amount of biotin and the fruits contained the smallest amount. Sixty-eight to 99 per cent of the biotin was present in the solids of the products analyzed. Folic acid measured as *Lactobacillus casei* and *Streptococcus lactis* [R] (later found to be *Streptococcus fecalis*) activity against crystalline vitamin B_c was found in highest quantity in the green vegetables. It was distributed about two-thirds in the solids and one-third in the liquid portions. The pyridoxine values were considerably higher than those for biotin and folic acid. The fish products were the best sources, and corn, spinach, and tomatoes were found to be secondary sources of this vitamin as compared to the fish products. The fruits had a low pyridoxine content. In general, approximately two-thirds of the pyridoxine content was found in the solid portion of the canned product.

REFERENCES

1. Thompson, M. L., Cunningham, E. and Snell, E. E. *The Nutritive Value of Canned Foods. IV. Riboflavin and Pantothenic Acid.* J. Nutrition **28**, 123-129, 1944.

2. Ives, M., Zepplin, M., Ames, S. R., Strong, F. M. and Elvehjem, C. A. *The Nutritive Value of Canned Foods. X. Further Studies on Riboflavin, Niacin, and Pantothenic Acid.* J. Am. Dietet. Assoc. **21**, 357-359, 1945.

3. Neilands, J. B., Strong, F. M. and Elvehjem, C. A. *The Nutritive Value of Canned Foods. XXV. Vitamin Content of Canned Fish Products.* J. Nutrition **34**, 633-643, 1947.

4. Ives, M., Pollard, A. E., Elvehjem, C. A. and Strong, F. M. *The Nutritive Value of Canned Foods. XVII. Pyridoxine, Biotin and "Folic Acid."* J. Nutrition **31**, 347-353, 1946.

STORAGE AND UTILIZATION OF CANNED FOODS

Chapter 1

STORAGE OF CANNED FOODS IN METAL CONTAINERS

A recent review (1) shows that canned food products are variable in their ability to withstand adverse quality changes during high temperature storage.

Under the usual storage conditions, canned foods show an excellent degree of stability against loss of quality (acceptability as food) or nutritive value. For maximum retention of quality and nutritive content, canned foods should be protected against prolonged exposure to high temperatures, a condition which operates to the detriment of many kinds of food and to which canned foods are not wholly immune. Surveys have shown that commercial warehousing conditions in most parts of the United States are favorable for canned foods, and that even in the hottest areas it is usually possible to protect such foods from the highest extremes of temperature.

The Relation of Storage to Vitamin Retention

The canned food nutrition program has sponsored projects at two universities to obtain more accurate and extensive information on the effects of constant temperatures on the vitamin content of canned foods. These projects were supplemented by a survey of temperatures existing in canned food warehouses throughout the United States. The data obtained support the recommendation frequently made to the canning industry that canned foods be stored under "cool" warehousing conditions. If canned food must be held at elevated temperatures, storage should be for as short a time as possible.

High Storage Temperatures—The effects of unusually high temperature storage on vitamin retention in canned foods were studied by Brenner *et al.* (2) and Guerrant *et al.* (3). The interest of these investigators was primarily on the effects of abnormally high temperatures such as were encountered in certain areas during the recent war. The findings show that a considerable degradation in certain vitamins in canned foods resulted from sustained storage temparatures of 90° F. or higher (4).

Moderate Sustained Temperatures—Guerrant *et al.* (5) studied the effect of constant temperatures of storage on asparagus, green beans, Lima beans, carrots, yellow and white corn, Alaska and sweet peas, spinach, apricots, and purple plums (prunes) using the temperatures 50°, 65°, and 80° F. for a period of two years. Moschette *et al.* (6) and Sheft *et al.* (7) tested the effects of the same conditions of storage on grapefruit juice, grapefruit segments, orange juice, peaches, pineapple juice, pineapple slices, tomato juice, and tomatoes for a period of two years.

Ascorbic Acid—For the canned foods studied under these conditions the retention of ascorbic acid in general decreased with increase in time and temperature of storage. The effects of these factors varied somewhat with the different canned foods. There appeared to be no consistent difference in the percentage of ascorbic acid retained by the respective products from different geographical areas. The ascorbic acid retentions for the one and two year storage periods are given in Table 13.

It can be concluded that canning offers an effective means of preservation of ascorbic acid in fruit and vegetable products even after extended periods of storage at moderate temperatures.

Carotene—Studies were made by the same observers on carotene retention under similar conditions of storage temperature and time. The retentions of carotene observed in canned foods during storage are given in Table 14.

TABLE 13

Retention of Ascorbic Acid in Various Canned Foods During Storage

Adapted from: Guerrant et al. (3), *Moschette et al.* (6), *and Sheft et al.* (7)

	Per Cent Retention					
	12 Months			24 Months		
Canned Foods	50°F.	65°F.	80°F.	50°F.	65°F.	80°F.
Apricots	96	93	85	94	90	56
Asparagus, green	97	94	89	93	91	86
Asparagus, white	96	94	87	90	87	82
Beans, green	92	90	85	88	81	74
Beans, Lima	100	98	95	86	83	78
Corn, yellow	98	94	89	92	89	81
Corn, white	98	92	86	90	88	78
Grapefruit juice	95	91	75	94	82	57
Grapefruit segments..	94	91	73	87	77	46
Orange juice	97	92	77	95	80	50
Peaches	98	85	72	98	80	53
Peas, Alaska	91	89	84	90	88	81
Peas, sweet	94	92	88	92	89	81
Pineapple juice	110	108	93	108	100	79
Pineapple, sliced	100	95	74	83	78	53
Spinach ....:	93	91	86	90	88	81
Tomatoes	95	94	82	89	87	70
Tomato juice	100	97	86	102	92	74

Retentions were good to excellent and the temperature of storage appeared to have only a limited effect. With most products, the adverse effect of storage temperature on retention of this vitamin was less marked than that of storage. For both the low acid and acid products, it was found that the highest temperature of storage (80° F.) did not always result in the lowest retentions of carotene.

Thiamine, Riboflavin, and Niacin—Extension of the studies previously discussed included investigations of thiamine, riboflavin, and niacin. The retentions for these B vitamins are shown in Table 15.

The thiamine retention for the low acid products studied (5) ranged from 46 per cent for green asparagus stored at 80° F. to 97 per cent for sweet peas stored at 50° F. Each

of the 26 packs of canned foods examined for thiamine retention, after being stored at the three temperatures for 24
months, showed the lowest vitamin retention when the product
had been stored at the highest temperature (80° F.). Likewise, for the other temperatures of storage studied, the lowest
temperature (50° F.) showed the highest retention of thiamine for most of the canned foods investigated, while the
intermediate temperature (65° F.) showed intermediate
values. One of the advantages of "cool" storage for canned
food is readily apparent from these studies.

TABLE 14

Retention of Carotene in Various Canned Foods During Storage

Adapted from: Guerrant et al. (3), Moschette et al. (6), and Sheft et al. (7)

| | Per Cent Retention | | | | | |
| | 12 Months | | | 24 Months | | |
Canned Foods	50°F.	65°F.	80°F.	50°F.	65°F.	80°F.
Apricots	94	85	83	91	84	76
Asparagus, green ..	97	88	85	88	84	76
Carrots, diced	94	97	93	90	95	91
Corn, yellow	85	87	84	69	72	87
Peaches	95	90	86	75	64	63
Peas, Alaska	97	95	91	95	93	89
Peas, sweet	98	92	91	94	90	90
Plums, purple, (prunes)	102	100	97	90	98	86
Spinach	91	90	84	80	80	81
Tomatoes	94	98	95	75	75	74
Tomato juice	98	100	99	94	97	98

The studies on the acid canned food products (6), orange
juice, grapefruit juice, grapefruit segments, pineapple juice,
pineapple slices, tomatoes, tomato juice, and peaches showed
that the losses of thiamine after two years' storage at 50° F.
and 65° F. were slight, not exceeding 13 per cent. After eight
months of storage there was no apparent loss in thiamine in
any canned fruit or fruit juice stored at 50° F. and 65° F.
After 12 months' storage at these temperatures, losses not

TABLE 15

Retention of Thiamine, Riboflavin, and Niacin in Various Canned Foods During Storage

Adapted from: Guerrant et al. (3), Moschette et al. (6), and Sheft et al. (7)

Canned Foods	Thiamine						Riboflavin						Niacin					
	Per Cent Retention						Per Cent Retention						Per Cent Retention					
	12 Months			24 Months			12 Months			24 Months			12 Months			24 Months		
	50°F.	65°F.	80°F.	50°F.	65°F.	80°F.	50°F.	65°F.	80°F.	50°F.	65°F.	80°F.	50°F.	65°F.	80°F.	50°F.	65°F.	80°F.
Asparagus, green	89	79	66	85	72	54	83		87	81	77	72	89	85	84	93	91	87
Asparagus, white	82	74	62	72	65	52	Not studied						96	94	97	96	98	97
Beans, green	92	86	78	82	80	67	62		69	62	57	42	83	81	80	86	86	86
Beans, Lima	88	82	74	87	76	66	88		91	75	75	70	101	100	99	100	97	100
Corn, white	97	85	78	94	89	71	Not studied						82	85	88	84	86	88
Corn, yellow	90	86	74	89	76	60	78		80	71	68	61	89	89	91	91	90	96
Grapefruit juice	99	100	93	99	94	84	Not studied						Not studied					
Orange juice	100	98	89	101	94	83	Not studied						Not studied					
Peaches	92	90	81	88	100	86	Not studied						101	102	101	100	98	99
Peas, Alaska	91	86	75	89	85	68	82		84	80	73	68	82	77	82	90	87	85
Peas, sweet	93	88	73	91	85	72	84		89	88	84	81	95	87	90	96	95	95
Pineapple juice	93	93	87	103	100	93	Not studied						Not studied					
Pineapple, sliced	97	96	89	102	103	89	Not studied						Not studied					
Plums, purple (prunes)	Not studied						78		82	84	82	76	95	93	103	86	91	95
Spinach	96	89	76	90	82	71	85		89	82	80	69	100	103	99	96	100	101
Tomatoes	94	93	82	91	87	70	91		95	96	98	97	91	93	93	88	88	85
Tomato juice	95	93	85	103	94	77	83		84	92	94	94	99	99	99	92	91	90

exceeding 7 per cent on the average were observed. At the highest temperature of storage after one year the retention of thiamine averaged 91 per cent for the citrus fruits and fruit juices; 88 per cent for pineapple and pineapple juice; 83 per cent for tomatoes and tomato juice; and 81 per cent for peaches.

In general, for the low acid products (5) the riboflavin content decreased with increases in both time and temperature of storage. The time effect appeared to be the more pronounced of the two factors. There was no evidence of any effect of the geographical area in which the products were grown, which might explain differences in riboflavin retention observed in different lots of the same product. For the acid products studied (7) tomatoes and tomato juice showed retentions of 97 and 94 per cent, respectively, after a two-year period at 80° F. In general, it may be concluded that riboflavin is well retained during storage of canned food products.

Niacin showed the greatest stability upon storage of canned foods of the three vitamin B factors studied. As with riboflavin, some differences were noted between different lots of the same product. In general, retentions were very good (85 per cent or over) for the two-year period. Where the lower retentions were noted, the time factor appeared to be more important than the temperature. It may be noted that niacin was retained very well in canned peaches, ranging from 96 to 100 per cent. In tomatoes, which showed retentions of 90 per cent or more at the end of 18 months, there was a final drop to 85 per cent at 80° F. Tomato juice retained 90 per cent or more during the entire period.

Commercial Warehouse Storage Studies

Findings on the effects of high, sustained storage temperatures on nutrients in canned foods led to inclusion in the canned food nutrition program of a project designed to determine actual temperature patterns in commercial canned food warehouses, and also to determine vitamin retention in canned foods under known warehousing conditions. The results of these studies may be briefly summarized.

Prevailing Temperatures—Monroe et al. (8) have reported a survey on the yearly temperatures prevailing in 79 canned food warehouses throughout the United States. Even in the hottest areas of the South, the average yearly warehouse temperature did not exceed 80° F. In the areas in which the greatest annual volume of canned food production is warehoused, the average yearly temperature was about 65° F.

Vitamin Retentions—In nine of the warehouse localities described above, samples of canned foods of known initial vitamin content were stored and samples periodically removed for analyses to determine the effects of storage at these localities. Results of these studies are contained in the publication of Guerrant et al. (5), Moschette et al. (6), and Sheft et al. (7). Table 16 indicates the ascorbic acid, thiamine, and caro-

TABLE 16

Vitamin Retentions in Canned Foods During Warehouse Storage

(12 Months' Storage Time)

Adapted from: Moschette et al. (6) and Guerrant et al. (5)

Locality	Storage Temp. Yearly Average	Storage Temp. Range	Per Cent Vitamin Retention Ascorbic Acid Orange Juice	Toma-toes	Peas	Thiamine Orange Juice	Toma-toes	Peas	Caro-tene Peas
	(°F.)	(°F.)							
Arizona	72	50-92	81	100	92	99	89	89	100
California, Central	66	51-87	92	102	94	96	86	92	100
California, North	70	54-104	86	105	94	99	88	85	97
District of Columbia	63	42-79	91	101	96	103	90	90	98
Florida	77	54-91	81	92	96	95	79	85	97
Illinois	59	28-92	90	98	96	99	89	89	98
Louisiana	77	50-98	73	83	92	96	83	83	97
Missouri	61	36-87	91	101	98	95	89	96	98
New York	58	30-78	96	106	93	98	96	91	97

tene retentions observed during one-year's warehouse storage of canned orange juice, tomatoes, and peas. Data on retentions after 18 and 24 months' storage are also available in the original publications.

The effects of sustained 50°, 65°, and 80° F. storage on vitamin retentions in a variety of canned foods have been previously discussed. For the products orange juice, tomatoes, and peas, the ascorbic acid, thiamine, and carotene retentions of the samples stored in warehouses were similar to those of companion samples stored for equal periods of time at constant temperatures corresponding to the warehouse yearly averages. These data also suggest the benefits of cool (not above 70° F.) storage.

Recommended Storage Conditions

The best conditions for storage of canned foods can be obtained by avoiding heat, extreme cold, and moisture. The United States Department of Agriculture Bulletin "Regulations for Warehousemen Storing Canned Foods" (9) instructs as follows:

"Do not stack canned foods generally known as acid products in close proximity to steam or hot water radiators or immediately under a metal roof.

Ventilate storage rooms so that a uniformly cool temperature will be maintained in the warehouse. Provide heat when necessary to avoid freezing."

These instructions are equally applicable to storage of canned foods in the home and apply to all canned foods whether or not they are in the acid category. Such foods should be kept at a moderately cool temperature in a dry storage place. If at all feasible, a storage temperature of 70° F. or below is desirable, as this storage temperature has been found to favor quality and vitamin retention in canned foods (1). Close proximity to steam pipes, radiators, stoves, or furnaces should be avoided. As shown, maintenance of canned food quality and nutritive value during storage are favored by employing these recommended storage practices.

REFERENCES

1. Feaster, J. F., Tompkins, M. D. and Pearce, W. E. *Effect of Storage on Vitamins and Quality in Canned Foods.* Food Research 14, 25-39, 1949.

2. Brenner, S., Wodicka, V. O. and Dunlop, S. G. *Effect of High Temperature Storage on the Retention of Nutrients in Canned Foods.* Food Technology 2, 207-221, 1948.

3. Guerrant, N. B., Vavich, M. G. and Dutcher, R. A. *Nutritive Value of Canned Foods. XIII. Influence of Temperature and Time of Storage on Vitamin Contents.* Ind. Eng. Chem. 37, 1240-1243, 1945.

4. Dunlop, S. G. *Open Storage of Foods in Desert Climates.* Proc. Inst. Food Technology 1945, 72-80.

5. Guerrant, N. B., Fardig, O. B., Vavich, M. G. and Ellenberger, H. E. *Nutritive Value of Canned Foods. XXVII. Influence of Temperature and Time of Storage on Vitamin Content.* Ind. Eng. Chem. 40, 2258-2263, 1948.

6. Moschette, D. S., Hinman, W. F. and Halliday, E. G. *Nutritive Value of Canned Foods. XXII. Effect of Time and Temperature of Storage on Vitamin Content of Commercially Canned Fruits and Fruit Juices (Stored 12 Months).* Ind. Eng. Chem. 39, 994-999, 1947.

7. Sheft, B. B., Griswold, R. M., Tarlowsky, E. and Halliday, E. G. *Nutritive Value of Canned Foods. XXVI. Effect of Time and Temperature of Storage on Vitamin Content of Commercially Canned Fruits and Fruit Juices (Stored 18 and 24 months).* Ind. Eng. Chem. 41, 144-145, 1949.

8. Monroe, K. H., Brighton, K. W. and Bendix, G. H. *The Nutritive Value of Canned Foods. XXVIII. Some Studies of Commercial Warehouse Temperatures with Reference to the Stability of Vitamins in Canned Foods.* Food Technology 3, 292-299, 1949.

9. United States Dept. Agr., Agricultural Marketing Service. *Regulations for Warehousemen Storing Canned Foods.* Service and Regulatory Announcement—Agr. Marketing Service No. 161, 1941, 19 p., U. S. Gov't Printing Office, Wash., D. C.

Chapter 2

PREPARATION OF FOOD FOR SERVING

The art of preparing food for serving is more than the production of a tasty dish attractively served. It includes the conservation of the essential nutrients. Improper cooking may take a heavy toll of these nutrients before the food reaches the table. The figures given for mineral and vitamin contents in food-composition tables are frequently based on

Canned foods make appetizing salads. Here, favorite tomato aspic is served in different combinations. It may be served, as shown, combined with sardines and nestled in a bed of crisp chicory; with cottage cheese and grapefruit sections; with avocado; or with marinated vegetables, according to preference.

raw food assays and therefore are higher than the actual amounts present when the food is eaten. This has been long realized by those who calculate the nutritive values of diets.

During the past few years more attention has been placed on preserving the nutritive values of foods. Modern transportation and refrigeration provide means of conserving the nutritive value of many perishable fruits and vegetables. Improved methods of commercial canning and freezing have helped in supplying adequate amounts of the essential nutrients in the daily dietary. But the nutritive benefits from technological improvements may be largely lost if the preparation of the food for the table is incorrectly done.

There are many factors involved in the effect of cooking on vitamin and mineral retention in the solid portion of vegetables. The most important factors appear to be as follows: Type of cooking method, amount of water used, length of cooking time, length of time required for the water to come to a boil after the vegetable is added, amount of cut surface, and nature of the vegetable itself.

The Cooking of Raw Vegetables

Methods which are used by homemakers for cooking raw vegetables include boiling in a large amount of water (approximately one to two cups for four servings); boiling or steaming in a small amount of water (approximately one-third to one-half cup for four servings); steaming in special utensils; baking; and cooking under steam pressure (1).

Data from several investigators clearly indicate that the retention of water-soluble vitamins in the vegetable itself is inversely proportional to the amount of cooking water used (2-4). It has been reported that no appreciable amounts of thiamine and ascorbic acid are actually destroyed when green beans, Lima beans, and peas were cooked by several investigators using proper cooking techniques (1, 5, 6). However, the rate of destruction of ascorbic acid is greatest during the first few minutes of cooking because of the presence of oxygen and enzymatic activity (7, 8). It is suggested that vegetables be cooked quickly in a small amount of water. Many investigators have reported as much as 80 per cent decrease in ascorbic acid when vegetables are cooked by improper techniques and the cooking liquid is discarded (9-11).

There are indications that the nature of the vegetable itself is a very important factor influencing water-soluble vitamin retention during cooking. Fresh legumes, roots, and tubers have been reported to lose less of some of the water-soluble vitamins during cooking than the flowery and leafy plants (12, 13). The length of time elapsing between the harvesting of the vegetables and consumption, as well as the conditions under which they have been stored, appear to have a direct influence upon the actual ascorbic acid content after cooking (4, 14).

Cooking does not seem to affect the carotene content of vegetables when assayed by the physico-chemical method used in most laboratories. However, it has been reported that cooking of foods decreases beta-carotene and increases neo-beta-carotenes U and B (15). Since these isomers are reported to have only 38 to 53 per cent of the physiological activity of beta-carotene, it would indicate that an actual loss does occur (16, 17). On the other hand, the absorption of carotene from some vegetables appears to be greater in the cooked than in the raw state (18). Experiments to determine the availability of carotene in foods are limited in number and conflicting in the results reported. Whether or not the greater absorption of carotene from cooked than from raw vegetables would offset the decreased physiological activity by the conversion of the carotenes to their isomers is a problem needing further research.

Important minerals such as calcium, phosphorus, and iron are also lost if the liquid portion of the cooked vegetables is discarded. Investigators have reported finding as much as 50 per cent of these minerals in the cooking liquid (10, 19).

Distribution of Nutrients in Canned Foods

Kramer (20) reported the distribution of certain nutrients between the solid and liquid portions of canned vegetables. Some of the mineral content was found in the liquid portion of the can. Less mature vegetables had more carbohydrates in the liquid than those that were more mature. The sugar of the less mature vegetables was more soluble than the starch of the more mature vegetables. The percentages of these nutrients which were found in the liquid portion are shown in Table 17.

TABLE 17

Percentage of Total Nutrients of Entire Can Contents Found In Liquid Portion

Adapted from: Kramer (20)

	Average Percentage of Total							
Canned Foods	Protein	Fat	Fiber	Ash	Carbo-hydrates	Calcium	Phos-phorus	Iron
Asparagus	14.3	4.4	3.9	33.1	27.6	30.3	19.5	27.0
Beans, green	15.4	*	4.4	37.2	22.7	16.6	26.7	24.5
Beans, Lima	10.3	0.9	0.7	35.9	9.2	27.9	28.4	32.3
Beets	31.2	*	1.5	31.7	28.7	11.1	31.4	24.9
Carrots	16.8	*	2.6	26.9	28.9	17.2	23.5	33.4
Corn	7.8	1.5	1.6	32.6	14.9	22.7	30.1	26.5
Peas	14.3	4.6	0.9	38.1	17.4	17.5	25.8	27.8
Spinach	6.3	*	1.3	23.8	22.1	0.7	27.6	11.5

* Insignificant quantity.

The University of Chicago group (21) have reported an investigation of the distribution of some of the water-soluble vitamins between the solid and liquid portions of several canned foods. Inspection of Table 18 demonstrates that sizable amounts of the water-soluble vitamins of canned foods are contained in liquid portions.

Preparation of Canned Vegetables

While it is true that canned foods may be served just as they come from the can, many of them are given further preparation. They should be prepared and served in ways that will best retain their nutritive value, flavor, and appearance. As a part of the canned foods nutrition program, studies were made on the preparation of canned foods for home and institution consumption.

TABLE 18

Percentage of Total Ascorbic Acid, Thiamine and Riboflavin of the Entire Can Contents Found in Liquid Portion

Adapted from: Brush et al. (21)

Canned Foods	Average Percentage of Total		
	Ascorbic Acid	Thiamine	Riboflavin
Asparagus	38	38	30
Beans, green	38	33	25
Beans, Lima	43	33	24
Carrots	33	31	24
Corn, white, whole grain	49	36	22
Corn, yellow, whole grain	47	35	25
Peas, sweet	38	33	29
Spinach	46	39	32
Apricots	47	50	45
Grapefruit segments	44	42	33
Peaches, cling	33	30	39
Peaches, freestone	51	39	44
Pears	32	43	31
Pineapple, sliced	41	40	34
Plums, purple (prunes)	51	49	47

Two methods for preparation of canned vegetables in the home were used in studies by Hinman *et al.* (22). In one, Method A, the liquid was drained from the vegetable and reduced by boiling to about one-third or one-fourth of its original volume and the drained vegetables added and heated. In Method B, the entire contents of the can (both vegetable and liquid) were heated, the liquid drained off before serving, and the food as served was then assayed.

The data from these studies listed in Table 19 can be summarized briefly and recommended methods for preparation of canned foods drawn from them. There was some ascorbic acid loss by either method used for small-scale preparation, but it was much less when the liquid was utilized. Boiling down the liquid was without significant effect upon thiamine and riboflavin; however, there was a 30 to 40 per cent loss of these factors when the liquid was discarded (Method B).

TABLE 19

Percentage Retention of Ascorbic Acid, Thiamine and Riboflavin During Small-Scale Preparation of Canned Foods for Serving

Adapted from: Hinman et al. (22)

| Canned Foods | Average Percentage of Total | | | | | |
| | Ascorbic Acid | | Thiamine | | Riboflavin | |
	Method A	Method B	Method A	Method B	Method A	Method B
Beans, green	82	49	98	61	102	65
Beans, Lima	62	39	97	62	93	72
Carrots	41	..	96	..	103	..
Corn, yellow, whole grain ...	49	35	92	62	98	63
Peas, sweet	51	30	100	63	102	65
Spinach	..	38	..	72	..	68
Tomatoes *	97		107		100	

* Entire contents of the can heated and served.

Effects of large-scale preparation—Hinman *et al.* (23) also investigated the effects of large-scale preparation on the ascorbic acid, thiamine and riboflavin content of canned vegetables. Nine products as listed in Table 20 were prepared for serving by boiling 30 minutes in a closed kettle. Since many who do large-quantity feeding hold their vegetables over heat before serving, a study of the effect of holding over steam for 1½ hours was investigated. Of the three vitamins studied, the retention of ascorbic acid was the most variable. In asparagus and tomatoes, there was no definite destruction of ascorbic acid during boiling for 30 minutes and holding for 1½ hours over steam. However, the asparagus was served with a slitted spoon, and the final retention of ascorbic acid in the served product was decreased in proportion to the amount of liquid discarded. There was no definite loss of either thiamine or riboflavin in any of the products during

TABLE 20

Percentage Retention of Ascorbic Acid, Thiamine and Riboflavin During Large-Scale Preparation* and Holding of Canned Vegetables for Serving

Adapted from: Hinman et al. (23)

Canned Food	Ascorbic Acid—Retention Served with Slitted Spoon		Thiamine—Retention Served with Slitted Spoon		Riboflavin—Retention Served with Slitted Spoon	
	Just After Heating	After Holding on Steam Table 1½ hrs.	Just After Heating	After Holding on Steam Table 1½ hrs.	Just After Heating	After Holding on Steam Table 1½ hrs.
Asparagus	72	68	72	71	76.	70
Beans, baked New Eng. style	..	..	91†	87†	74†	71†
Beans, baked with tomato sauce	..	..	88†	84†	96†	79†
Beans, green, cut	30	12	60	58	70	64
Beans, Lima, green	29	9	72	71	72	66
Carrots	30	21	74	70	80	82
Corn, yellow, whole grain	..	..	56	53	70	68
Spinach	52	45	66	66	69	66
Tomatoes	97†	88†	82†	79†	103†	77†

* Boiled 30 minutes, tested immediately.
† Whole contents of can served.

preparation for serving. However, when some liquid was discarded as in serving with a slitted spoon, the losses of these vitamins were directly related to their concentration in the boiled liquid and the proportion of liquid which was discarded.

Recommendations for Preparing Canned Foods

The studies reported give clear indication that proper preparation of canned food is important from the standpoint of optimum nutrient retention. As a result of the studies related here, and of other studies, the following recommendations have gained wide acceptance.

Canned foods should not be overcooked in preparation. Long periods of cooking before serving may result in the destruction of certain of the nutrients as well as in an unappetizing appearance of the food. Since canned foods are cooked during processing, they need only be thoroughly heated for table preparation.

For institutional food service, preparation in small quantities and immediate use, or the shortest times of steam table holdings, are found to be best for retention of nutrients. When the liquid is not served with the food, it should be used in other ways.

Just as it is now generally recommended that liquids be used when market foods are cooked in the home, it is likewise recommended that the liquid from canned foods be utilized. The use of the liquid content in food preparation is important for maximum utilization of the water-soluble nutrients. There is another reason for using the liquid from canned foods and that is the added and improved flavor which results from the use. When baking and creaming vegetables, the liquid may be used as part of the sauce. The liquid and oil from canned seafood make nutritious and flavorsome sauces and the oil is excellent in French dressing for seafood salad.

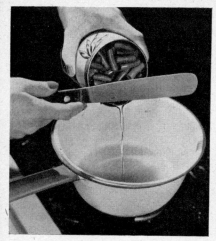

Courtesy American Can Company

A convenient method of conserving the liquid portion of canned foods —in this case canned green beans—is illustrated. A flat knife may be used instead of a spatula.

The modern recommended method for preparing buttered canned vegetables in the home is as follows: Drain the liquid from the vegetable into a saucepan; boil until reduced in volume to about a half or a third cup; add vegetables, butter, and seasonings. Heat, but do not overcook. The concentrated liquid adheres to the vegetable and is eaten with it.

Many canned foods, such as fruits, soup, ready-made entrees, pork and beans, or baked beans, juices, purees, and sauces are normally wholly consumed and the problem of a special use of liquid does not exist. Reference may be made to publications of the Home Economics Division of the National Canners Association or those of various canning companies and can manufacturing companies for further recommended methods for preparing canned foods (24-26).

REFERENCES

1. McIntosh, J. and Jones, E. *The Effect of Various Cooking Methods on Vitamin Retention in Vegetables, Thiamine and Ascorbic Acid.* Food Technology 1, 258-263, 1947.

2. Barnes, B., Tressler, D. K. and Fenton, F. *Thiamine Content of Fresh and Frozen Peas and Corn Before and After Cooking.* Food Research 8, 420-427, 1943.

3. Ireson, M. G. and Eheart, M. S. *Ascorbic Acid Losses in Cooked Vegetables; Cooked Uncovered in a Large Amount of Water and Covered in a Small Amount of Water.* J. Home Econ. 36, 160-165, 1944.

4. Gleim, E. G., Tressler, D. K. and Fenton, F. *Ascorbic Acid, Thiamine, Riboflavin and Carotene Contents of Asparagus and Spinach in the Fresh, Stored, and Frozen States, Both Before and After Cooking.* Food Research 9, 471-490, 1944.

5. Fincke, M. L., Little, R., Redelings, E. and Perkins, J. *Further Studies of the Thiamine Values of Frozen Peas.* Food Research 8, 123-127, 1943.

6. Mack, G. L., Tapley, W. T. and King, C. G. *Vitamin C in Vegetables. X. Snap Beans.* Food Research 4, 309-316, 1939.

7. Fenton, F., Tressler, D. K. and King, C. G. *Losses of Vitamin C During the Cooking of Peas.* J. Nutrition 12, 285-295, 1936.

8. Fenton, F. and Tressler, D. K. *Losses of Vitamin C During the Cooking of Certain Vegetables.* J. Home Econ. 30, 717-722, 1938.

9. Van Duyne, F. O., Chase, J. T., Fanska, J. R. and Simpson, J. I. *Effect of Certain Home Practices on Reduced Ascorbic Acid Content of Peas, Rhubarb, Snap Beans, Soybeans, and Spinach.* Food Research 12, 439-448, 1947.

10. Hewston, E. M., Dawson, E. H., Alexander, L. M. and Orent-Keiles, E. *Vitamin and Mineral Content of Certain Foods as Affected by Home Preparation.* Misc. Pub. No. 628, U. S. Dept. of Agr., January, 1948.

11. Sutherland, C. K., Halliday, E. G. and Hinman, W. F. *Vitamin Retention and Acceptability of Fresh Vegetables Cooked by Four Household Methods and by an Institutional Method.* Food Research 12, 496-509, 1947.

12. Russell, W. C., Taylor, M. W. and Beuk, J. F. *The Nicotinic Acid Content of Common Fruits and Vegetables as Prepared for Human Consumption.* J. Nutrition 25, 275-284, 1943.

13. Fenton, F. *Vitamin C Retention on Criterion of Quality and Nutritive Value in Vegetables.* J. Am. Dietet. Assoc. 16, 524-535, 1940.

14. Eheart, J. F., Speirs, M. and Cochran, H. L. *Ascorbic Acid Content of Lima Beans I, Effect of Methods of Storage II, Effect of Length of Time of Cooking.* Southern Region Prog. Note 4 (Ga., Miss., S. C., Va., and Va. Truck Stas., Exp. Stas. and U. S. Vegetable Breeding Lab. Cooperating). (Issued by Va. Sta.) 2 pp., 1944.

15. Kammerer, A. R., Fraps, G. S. and Meinke, W. W. *Constituents of the Crude Carotene of Certain Human Foods.* Food Research **10**, 66-71, 1945.

16. Deuel, H. J., Johnston, C., Sumner, E., Polgar, A. and Zechmeister, L. *Steriochemical Configuration and Provitamin A Activity I. Alltrans Beta-Carotene and Neo-Beta-Carotene U.* Arch. Biochem. **5**, 107-114, 1944.

17. Deuel, H. J., Johnston, C., Meserve, E. R., Polgar, A. and Zechmeister, L. *Steriochemical Configuration and Provitamin A Activity IV. Neo-Alpha-Carotene B., and Neo-Beta-Carotene B.* Arch. Biochem. **7**, 247-255, 1945.

18. Eriksen, B. and Höygaard, A. *The Absorption of Carotene in Man.* Klin Wochshr. **20**, 200-201, 1941, C. A. **36**, 7075, 1942.

19. Brinkman, E. V. S., Halliday, E. G., Hinman, W. F., and Hamner, R. J. *Effect of Various Cooking Methods Upon Subjective Qualities and Nutritive Values of Vegetables.* Food Research **7**, 300-305, 1942.

20. Kramer, A. *The Nutritive Value of Canned Foods. VIII. Distribution of Proximate and Mineral Nutrients in the Drained and Liquid Portions of Canned Vegetables.* J. Am. Dietet. Assoc. **21**, 354-356, 1945.

21. Brush, M. K., Hinman, W. F. and Halliday, E. G. *The Nutritive Value of Canned Foods. V. Distribution of Water Soluble Vitamins Between Solid and Liquid Portions of Canned Vegetables and Fruits.* J. Nutrition **28**, 131-140, 1944.

22. Hinman, W. F., Brush, M. K. and Halliday, E. G. *The Nutritive Value of Canned Foods. VII. Effect of Small-Scale Preparation on the Ascorbic Acid, Thiamine and Riboflavin Content of Commercially-Canned Vegetables.* J. Am. Dietet. Assoc. **21**, 7-10, 1945.

23. Hinman, W. F., Brush, M. K. and Halliday, E. G. *The Nutritive Value of Canned Foods. VI. Effect of Large-Scale Preparation for Serving on the Ascorbic Acid, Thiamine, and Riboflavin Content of Commercially-Canned Vegetables.* J. Am. Dietet. Assoc. **20**, 752-756, 1944.

24. Home Economics Department, National Canners Association. *Tempting Recipes Using Canned Foods.* Washington, D. C., 1946.

25. Home Economics Department, National Canners Association. *Canned Food Recipes for Serving Fifty.* Washington, D. C., 1946.

26. Home Economics Department, National Canners Association. *School Lunch Recipes Using Canned Food—25-50 Servings.* Washington, D. C., 1949.

Appendix

TABLES OF NUTRITIVE VALUES OF CANNED FOODS

Table I

PROXIMATE COMPOSITION OF SOME COMMER-
CIALLY CANNED FOODS

Because of differences both in the composition of canning varieties and the variations in the composition of the same variety under varied growing conditions and because of certain differences in canning practices, commercially canned foods may show variations in composition. The following table, therefore, has been arranged to indicate maximum, minimum, and average values for each product.

The style of pack often influences the proximate analysis, especially in the case of the fruits and vegetables to which packing media containing sugar and/or salt are commonly added. Wherever possible, the type of product is indicated by use of the following symbols:

WP—Water packed	NS—No sugar added
JP—Juice packed	NSA—No salt added
BP—Brine packed	AS—Added sugar
VP—Vacuum packed	SA—Salt added
SYP.P—Syrup packed	EP—Edible portion

Data included in this table have been compiled from several sources including analyses submitted by manufacturers to the Council on Foods and Nutrition of the American Medical Association; bulletins published by various state food regulatory commissions; tables published by United States Government Agencies; the third edition of the *Canned Foods Reference Manual* of the American Can Company; and findings made in the N.C.A.-C.M.I. Nutrition Program. Data published prior to July 1, 1949 are included in the compilation.

For many products, acids and/or other constituents in addition to ash, fat, protein, and crude fiber were determined and included in calculating carbohydrates by difference.

TABLE I

Proximate Composition of Some Commercially Canned Foods

Canned Foods	No. of Analyses		Total Solids %	Ash %	Fat (E.E.) %	Protein (Nx6.25) %	Crude Fiber %	Carbohydrates by diff. %	Calories per 100 grams	Calories per pound
Apple Juice, NS	2	Max.	11.5	0.2	0.2	0.1	trace	11.2	47	210
		Min.	11.4	0.1	...	trace	trace	11.1	44	200
		Ave.	11.5	0.2	0.1	0.1	trace	11.2	45	200
Apple Sauce, NS	3	Max.	12.9	0.2	0.3	0.3	0.8	11.5	47	210
		Min.	10.6	0.2	trace	0.2	0.5	9.0	40	180
		Ave.	11.9	0.2	0.2	0.3	0.6	10.2	43	200
Apple Sauce, AS	2	Max.	25.0	0.2	0.1	0.2	0.5	23.6	96	440
		Min.	23.5	0.2	0.1	0.2	0.5	22.5	92	420
		Ave.	24.3	0.2	0.1	0.2	0.5	23.1	94	430
Apple Sauce, chopped, AS	1	...	...	...	...	...	...	...	...	...
		...	...	...	...	...	...	...	...	...
		...	14.2	0.4	0.7	0.1	2.1	10.9	50	230
Apple Sauce, strained, AS	5	Max.	16.2	0.4	0.7	0.3	2.1	14.7	58	260
		Min.	13.9	0.2	0.02	0.1	0.5	10.9	49	220
		Ave.	15.2	0.3	0.3	0.2	0.9	11.5	54	240
Apple Sauce, strained, AS, SA	1	...	...	...	...	...	...	...	...	...
		...	...	...	...	...	...	...	...	...
		...	20.8	0.8	0.8	0.2	1.0	17.5	78	350
Apricots, WP	4	Max.	9.6	0.4	0.1	0.6	0.3	7.6	33	150
		Min.	7.8	0.3	0.1	0.4	0.3	6.0	26	120
		Ave.	8.5	0.4	0.1	0.5	0.3	6.9	30	140
Apricots, JP	2	Max.	13.8	0.7	0.2	0.6	0.5	12.0	51	230
		Min.	12.7	0.7	0.1	0.4	0.4	10.9	47	210
		Ave.	13.3	0.7	0.2	0.5	0.5	11.5	49	220
Apricots, SYP.P.	52	Max.	31.7	1.3	0.3	0.9	0.6	30.4	127	580
		Min.	10.3	0.3	0.01	0.2	0.3	8.9	39	180
		Ave.	26.0	0.6	0.1	0.5	0.4	21.0	87	390
Apricots, chopped, AS, SA	1	...	...	...	...	...	...	...	...	...
		...	...	...	...	...	...	...	...	...
		...	18.7	0.6	trace	0.7	0.6	16.8	70	320
Apricots, chopped, NS	1	...	...	...	...	...	...	...	...	...
		...	...	...	...	...	...	...	...	...
		...	26.1	1.1	0.1	1.3	0.9	22.7	97	440

TABLE I *(Continued)*

Proximate Composition of Some Commercially Canned Foods

Canned Foods	No. of Analyses		Total Solids %	Ash %	Fat (E.E.) %	Protein (Nx6.25) %	Crude Fiber %	Carbohydrates by diff. %	Calories per 100 grams	Calories per pound
Apricots, strained, NS	5	Max.	20.7	1.1	1.0	2.3	2.4	16.5	78	350
		Min.	12.4	0.5	0.1	0.7	0.6	10.1	45	200
		Ave.	15.7	0.8	0.4	1.1	1.0	12.2	57	260
Apricots, strained, AS	2	Max.	24.2	1.0	0.1	1.3	0.8	21.0	90	410
		Min.	22.5	0.7	trace	0.7	0.5	20.6	85	390
		Ave.	23.4	0.9	0.1	1.0	0.7	20.8	88	400
Apricot juice, NS	1	...	...	...	...	...	...	...	...	...
		...	...	...	...	...	...	...	...	...
		...	11.6	0.5	0.4	0.5	trace	10.2	47	210
Asparagus, white, cut spears	4	Max.	6.8	1.7	0.4	2.0	0.6	3.0	20	90
		Min.	6.2	1.2	0.2	1.5	0.5	2.2	19	90
		Ave.	6.5	1.4	0.3	1.7	0.5	2.6	20	90
Asparagus, white, spears	12	Max.	7.3	1.7	0.5	2.2	0.7	3.4	23	100
		Min.	6.0	1.0	0.2	1.3	0.5	2.3	18	80
		Ave.	6.7	1.5	0.4	1.6	0.6	2.8	20	90
Asparagus, green, spears	23	Max.	7.7	1.8	0.4	2.3	0.6	4.2	28	130
		Min.	5.9	0.7	0.2	1.5	0.1	2.0	17	80
		Ave.	6.7	1.3	0.3	2.0	0.5	2.6	21	100
Asparagus, green, cut spears	18	Max.	7.3	1.9	0.4	2.4	0.6	3.1	22	100
		Min.	5.0	0.8	0.1	1.1	0.4	1.6	14	60
		Ave.	6.1	1.3	0.3	1.6	0.5	2.4	19	90
Asparagus, WP	4	Max.	6.7	0.9	0.2	2.8	0.7	2.9	24	110
		Min.	4.9	0.4	0.1	1.5	0.4	1.9	14	60
		Ave.	6.0	0.6	0.2	2.1	0.6	2.6	20	90
Asparagus, strained	**	...	...	...	...	...	...	...	...	...
		...	...	...	...	...	...	...	...	...
		Ave.	8.0	1.4	0.1	2.0	0.5	4.0	26	120
Beans, green and wax, WP	5	Max.	5.2	0.8	0.7	1.4	0.5	3.1	20	90
		Min.	4.4	0.4	0.1	0.9	0.4	2.1	15	70
		Ave.	4.9	0.5	0.3	1.1	0.5	2.5	17	80
Beans, green and wax, cut, SA	113	Max.	8.3	1.7	0.5	1.5	0.9	5.3	28	130
		Min.	5.2	0.6	0.02	0.6	0.2	2.0	14	60
		Ave.	6.5	1.2	0.1	1.1	0.7	3.4	19	90

** Number of analyses unknown.

TABLE I *(Continued)*

Proximate Composition of Some Commercially Canned Foods

Canned Foods	No. of Analyses		Total Solids %	Ash %	Fat (E.E.) %	Protein (Nx6.25) %	Crude Fiber %	Carbo-hydrates by diff. %	Calories per 100 grams	Calories per pound
Beans, green, whole, SA	2	Max.	6.6	1.4	0.3	0.9	0.5	3.4	20	90
		Min.	6.0	1.3	0.2	0.8	0.5	3.2	18	80
		Ave.	6.3	1.4	0.2	0.9	0.5	3.3	19	90
Beans, green, chopped, SA	4	Max.	8.9	1.2	0.7	1.6	1.3	5.0	29	130
		Min.	6.6	0.7	trace	1.1	0.8	3.2	20	90
		Ave.	7.7	0.9	0.3	1.3	0.1	3.7	25	110
Beans, green, strained, NSA, NS	6	Max.	.7.7	0.7	0.2	2.0	1.8	4.8	25	110
		Min.	5.2	0.4	0.1	1.0	0.6	3.1	17	80
		Ave.	6.7	0.5	0.1	1.5	0.9	3.8	20	90
Beans, green and wax, strained, SA	8	Max.	8.5	1.4	0.2	1.6	1.1	5.0	28	130
		Min.	5.8	0.6	0.04	1.1	0.6	2.8	17	80
		Ave.	7.3	1.0	0.1	1.3	0.8	4.0	23	100
Beans, Lima, WP	3	Max.	22.6	0.8	0.4	4.7	1.7	16.0	85	390
		Min.	17.9	0.6	0.2	3.6	1.0	11.8	65	290
		Ave.	18.5	0.7	0.3	4.3	1.3	13.4	74	340
Beans, Lima, SA	54	Max.	22.5	2.0	0.4	5.7	2.7	15.0	81	370
		Min.	15.1	0.9	0.1	3.2	0.9	6.6	55	250
		Ave.	19.3	1.4	0.3	4.1	1.3	12.2	68	310
Beans, baked, with pork and tomato sauce	1	...	...	...	...	...	...	...	...	...
		...	...	...	...	...	...	...	...	...
		...	31.5	1.8	2 2	5.9	1.9	19.7	122	550
Beans, baked, tomato sauce, no pork	2	Max.	29.0	2.1	1.0	5.9	1.3	20.0	108	490
		Min.	27.9	0.9	0.7	5.0	1.1	19.0	106	480
		Ave.	28.5	1.5	0.9	5.5	1.2	19.5	107	480
Beans, baked, New England, with pork	2	Max.	35.7	1.8	3.7	6.1	2.6	21.4	144	650
		Min.	29.2	0.6	1.9	5.3	1.9	19.5	116	520
		Ave.	32.5	1.2	2.8	5.7	2.3	20.5	130	590
Beans, red kidney	**	...	...	...	...	...	...	...	..	...
		...	...	...	...	...	...	...	...	...
		Ave.	24.0	1.5	0.4	5.7	0.9	15.5	92	420
Beef, corned, medium fat	**	...	...	...	...	...	...	...	...	...
		...	...	...	...	...	...	...	...	...
		Ave.	40.7	3.4	12.0	25.3	...	trace	209	950

** Number of analyses unknown.

TABLE I *(Continued)*

Proximate Composition of Some Commercially Canned Foods

Canned Foods	No. of Analyses		Total Solids %	Ash %	Fat (E.E.) %	Protein (Nx6.25) %	Crude Fiber %	Carbohydrates by diff. %	Calories per 100 grams	Calories per pound
Beef, roast	**	...	...	...	...	...	...	...	...	...
		...	...	...	...	...	...	...	...	...
		Ave.	40.0	2.0	13.0	25.0	...	...	216	980
Beef and gravy	**	...	...	...	...	...	...	...	...	...
		...	...	...	...	...	...	...	...	...
		Ave.	34.7	...	11.7	19.4	...	1.3	188	850
Beef, chopped, SA	1	...	...	...	...	...	...	...	...	...
		...	...	...	...	...	...	...	...	...
		...	25.3	1.5	1.7	22.6	...	...	105	480
Beef, strained, SA	3	Max.	21.4	1.6	3.0	17.7	0.1	1.4	81	370
		Min.	17.5	0.9	0.5	14.4	trace	1.0	67	300
		Ave.	19.3	1.2	1.5	15.9	0.1	1.2	74	340
Beef broth, strained, SA	2	Max.	2.3	1.1	trace	1.7	trace	0.2	5	20
		Min.	1.8	1.1	trace	0.8	trace	trace	4	20
		Ave.	2.1	1.1	trace	1.3	trace	0.1	4	20
Beet juice, NS, NSA	1	...	...	...	...	...	...	...	...	...
		...	...	...	...	...	...	...	...	...
		...	8.3	0.6	0.1	0.6	trace	7.0	31	140
Beets, whole, WP	4	Max.	18.3	1.1	0.2	1.6	0.9	16.5	70	320
		Min.	9.9	0.5	0.1	0.7	0.5	7.9	36	160
		Ave.	13.4	0.7	0.1	1.2	0.7	10.8	49	220
Beets, whole, SA	5	Max.	11.4	0.9	0.1	1.0	0.6	8.9	40	180
		Min.	8.4	0.8	0.1	0.7	0.5	6.2	28	130
		Ave.	9.3	0.8	0.1	0.8	0.5	7.0	32	150
Beets, chopped, SA	3	Max.	9.7	1.2	0.2	1.0	0.6	7.5	35	160
		Min.	8.5	0.7	trace	0.7	0.5	5.7	29	130
		Ave.	9.1	1.0	0.1	0.8	0.6	6.5	31	140
Beets, strained, NSA	6	Max.	12.6	1.0	0.2	1.7	1.4	9.5	44	200
		Min.	7.8	0.5	trace	0.9	0.5	4.9	25	110
		Ave.	10.7	0.8	0.1	1.3	0.8	7.7	37	170
Beets, strained, SA	4	Max.	14.3	1.5	0.2	1.4	2.4	10.9	51	230
		Min.	8.7	0.4	trace	0.9	0.5	5.4	26	120
		Ave.	10.7	1.1	0.1	1.2	1.0	7.4	33	150

** Number of analyses unknown.

TABLE I *(Continued)*

Proximate Composition of Some Commercially Canned Foods

Canned Foods	No. of Analyses		Total Solids %	Ash %	Fat (E.E.) %	Protein (Nx6.25) %	Crude Fiber %	Carbohydrates by diff. %	Calories per 100 grams	Calories per pound
Blackberries, WP	1	...	...	...	...	...	...	...	...	...
		...	...	...	...	...	...	...	...	...
		...	11.0	0.4	0.8	1.0	2.0	6.8	38	170
Blackberries, JP	2	Max.	13.6	0.5	0.5	0.9	3.5	9.3	45	200
		Min.	12.0	0.3	0.1	0.8	2.1	7.1	33	150
		Ave.	12.8	0.4	0.3	0.9	2.8	8.2	39	180
Blackberries, SYP.P	6	Max.	27.0	0.3	0.2	0.9	3.5	23.1	97	440
		Min.	20.2	0.3	0.1	0.7	2.6	15.8	68	310
		Ave.	24.0	0.3	0.2	0.7	2.9	19.8	84	380
Blackberry juice, NS	1	...	...	...	...	...	...	...	...	...
		...	...	...	...	...	...	...	...	...
		...	14.6	0.4	0.6	0.1	trace	13.5	60	270
Blueberries, WP	6	Max.	12.8	0.2	0.2	0.7	0.5	12.3	53	240
		Min.	9.1	0.1	0.1	0.5	0.4	7.8	35	160
		Ave.	11.5	0.2	0.2	0.6	0.4	10.2	45	200
Blueberries, JP	2	Max.	13.1	0.4	0.6	0.7	1.5	9.9	48	220
		Min.	11.1	0.2	0.4	0.4	1.1	9.0	41	190
		Ave.	12.1	0.3	0.5	0.6	1.3	9.5	45	200
Blueberries, SYP.P	**	...	...	...	...	...	...	...	...	...
		...	...	...	...	...	...	...	...	...
		Ave.	27.0	0.2	0.4	0.4	1.0	25.0	109	490
Carrot juice, NS, NSA	1	...	...	...	...	...	...	...	...	...
		...	...	...	...	...	...	...	...	...
		...	6.8	0.3	0.2	0.3	trace	6.0	27	120
Carrots, WP	2	Max.	9.7	0.8	0.3	1.0	1.0	6.6	33	150
		Min.	8.3	0.3	0.2	0.5	0.8	6.5	30	140
		Ave.	9.0	0.6	0.3	0.8	0.9	6.6	32	150
Carrots, SA	39	Max.	10.0	1.1	0.4	0.9	0.7	7.0	34	150
		Min.	6.7	0.7	0.1	0.4	0.4	4.2	22	100
		Ave.	8.2	0.9	0.2	0.7	0.6	5.8	28	130
Carrots, chopped, NSA	1	...	...	...	...	...	...	...	...	...
		...	...	...	...	...	...	...	...	...
		...	6.9	0.8	0.1	0.9	0.7	4.4	22	100

** Number of analyses unknown.

TABLE I *(Continued)*

Proximate Composition of Some Commercially Canned Foods

Canned Foods	No. of Analyses		Total Solids %	Ash %	Fat (E.E.) %	Protein (Nx6.25) %	Crude Fiber %	Carbo-hydrates by diff. %	Calories per 100 grams	Calories per pound
Carrots, chopped, SA	4	Max.	7.3	1.0	0.4	0.7	0.7	4.9	21	100
		Min.	6.3	0.6	0.1	0.5	0.5	4.2	22	100
		Ave.	7.0	0.8	0.2	0.6	0.6	4.5	22	100
Carrots, strained, NSA	6	Max.	11.1	0.8	0.2	1.0	0.7	8.5	39	180
		Min.	7.4	0.4	0.1	0.6	0.6	5.2	25	110
		Ave.	8.4	0.6	0.2	0.8	0.6	6.3	30	140
Carrots, strained, SA	7	Max.	14.3	1.2	0.2	2.4	1.3	9.9	50	230
		Min.	5.4	0.6	trace	0.4	0.4	3.9	18	80
		Ave.	8.4	0.9	0.1	0.9	0.8	5.8	28	130
Cauliflower, WP	1	...	...	...	...	...	...	...	...	...
		...	4.9	0.5	0.4	1.1	0.7	2.2	17	80
Celery, strained, SA	1	...	...	...	...	...	...	...	...	...
		...	4.2	1.0	0.1	0.6	0.6	1.9	11	50
Celery, strained, NSA, NS	2	Max.	6.4	1.0	0.2	1.0	0.8	3.7	19	90
		Min.	5.9	1.0	0.1	0.8	0.8	2.9	17	80
		Ave.	6.3	1.0	0.2	0.9	0.8	3.3	18	80
Cherries, black, EP, WP	1	...	...	...	...	...	...	...	...	...
		...	19.0	0.4	0.8	0.7	0.2	16.9	78	350
Cherries, black, JP	1	...	...	...	...	...	...	...	...	...
		...	18.9	0.5	0.1	0.5	0.1	17.7	74	340
Cherries, red sour pitted, WP	5	Max.	13.8	0.5	0.5	1.0	0.2	12.2	54	240
		Min.	12.0	0.4	0.1	0.6	0.1	10.4	44	200
		Ave.	13.2	0.4	0.3	0.8	0.1	11.5	50	230
Cherries, red, sour pitted, JP	2	Max.	15.8	0.5	1.0	1.0	0.2	13.6	65	290
		Min.	12.6	0.4	0.8	0.8	0.1	10.0	53	240
		Ave.	14.2	0.5	0.9	0.9	0.2	11.8	59	270
Cherries, red, sour pitted, SYP.P	**	...	...	...	...	...	...	...	...	...
		Ave.	29.8	0.6	0.1	0.6	0.2	28.3	117	530

** Number of analyses unknown.

TABLE I *(Continued)*

Proximate Composition of Some Commercially Canned Foods

Canned Foods	No. of Analyses		Total Solids %	Ash %	Fat (E.E.) %	Protein (Nx6.25) %	Crude Fiber %	Carbohydrates by diff. %	Calories per 100 grams	Calories per pound
Cherries, Royal Anne, WP	2	Max.	13.8	0.3	0.5	0.6	0.2	12.3	52	240
		Min.	10.7	0.3	trace	0.6	0.1	9.2	44	200
		Ave.	12.3	0.3	0.3	0.6	0.2	10.8	48	220
Cherries, Royal Anne, JP	2	Max.	17.4	0.6	0.1	1.0	0.2	15.5	67	300
		Min.	15.3	0.5	0.1	0.8	0.2	13.7	59	270
		Ave.	16.4	0.6	0.1	0.9	0.2	14.6	63	290
Cherries, Royal Anne, EP, SYP.P	**	...	...	...	...	...	...	...	...	...
		...	...	...	...	...	...	...	...	...
		Ave.	21.9	0.4	0.1	0.6	0.2	20.6	86	390
Cherry juice, red, NS	1	...	...	...	...	...	...	...	...	...
		...	...	...	...	...	...	...	...	...
		...	12.3	0.3	0.6	0.5	trace	10.9	51	230
Chicken, meat only	**	...	...	...	...	...	...	...	...	...
		...	...	...	...	...	...	...	...	...
		Ave.	38.1	2.4	8.0	29.8	...	...	192	870
Chicken, meat and broth	**	...	...	...	...	...	...	...	...	...
		...	...	...	...	...	...	...	...	...
		Ave.	29.8	1.6	3.4	23.2	...	...	124	560
Chili con carne without beans	**	...	...	...	...	...	...	...	...	...
		...	...	...	...	...	...	...	...	...
		Ave.	33.7	...	14.6	10.2	...	6.4	198	900
Clams, long and round	2	Max.	17.1	2.3	1.3	10.5	...	3.0	61	280
		Min.	15.5	1.0	0.8	9.0	...	2.9	59	270
		Ave.	16.3	1.7	1.1	9.8	...	3.0	60	270
Clam bouillon	**	...	...	...	...	...	...	...	...	...
		...	...	...	...	...	...	...	...	...
		Ave.	5.2	2.3	...	1.4	...	1.5	12	50
Corn, cream style, WP	1	...	...	...	...	...	...	...	...	...
		...	...	...	...	...	...	...	...	...
		...	15.1	0.5	0.7	1.8	0.5	11.6	60	270
Corn, cream style, white SA	11	Max.	28.1	1.2	0.8	2.5	0.7	23.3	108	490
		Min.	20.6	0.8	0.4	1.9	0.3	16.2	79	360
		Ave.	24.5	1.0	0.6	2.2	0.6	19.1	91	410

** Number of analyses unknown.

TABLE I *(Continued)*

Proximate Composition of Some Commercially Canned Foods

Canned Foods	No. of Analyses		Total Solids %	Ash %	Fat (E.E.) %	Protein (Nx6.25) %	Crude Fiber %	Carbo-hy-drates by diff. %	Calories per 100 grams	Calories per pound
Corn, cream style, yellow SA	27	Max.	27.8	1.6	1.1	2.7	0.8	23.0	108	490
		Min.	19.2	0.8	0.3	1.9	0.3	15.2	80	360
		Ave.	24.8	1.1	0.6	2.1	0.5	19.5	93	420
Corn, whole grain, white	76	Max.	23.2	1.2	1.1	2.8	1.4	19.3	89	400
		Min.	15.0	0.4	0.3	1.2	0.4	11.1	52	240
		Ave.	18.2	0.8	0.6	1.9	0.6	14.3	68	310
Corn, whole grain, yellow	114	Max.	24.1	1.5	1.0	3.1	1.5	18.9	99	450
		Min.	16.0	0.6	0.4	1.2	0.3	12.1	61	280
		Ave.	19.6	1.0	0.6	1.9	0.5	15.6	76	340
Corn, whole grain, yellow VP, SA	6	Max.	26.5	1.3	0.6	2.8	0.9	21.5	102	460
		Min.	23.2	0.9	0.5	2.2	0.6	18.5	88	400
		Ave.	24.5	1.1	0.5	2.5	0.8	19.6	93	420
Corn, whole grain, VP, NS, NSA	1	...	...	...	...	...	...	...	...	...
		...	26.1	0.5	1.4	3.5	0.6	20.1	107	480
Crab, Japanese	5	Max.	22.5	1.7	2.7	17.9	...	...	96	440
		Min.	22.0	1.3	2.4	17.0	...	...	89	400
		Ave.	22.4	1.5	2.5	17.4	...	...	92	420
Crab, Pacific Coast	22	Max.	23.4	2.0	3.8	18.0	...	...	106	480
		Min.	21.7	1.4	1.8	16.2	...	...	81	370
		Ave.	22.4	1.7	3.0	17.1	...	...	96	440
Cranberry sauce, AS	**	...	...	...	...	...	...	...	...	...
		Ave.	51.9	0.1	0.3	0.1	0.4	51.0	208	950
Cranberry sauce, strained, AS	1	...	...	...	...	...	...	...	...	...
		...	45.4	0.3	0.3	0.2	0.4	44.2	180	820
Figs, WP	3	Max.	12.6	0.4	0.2	0.5	0.8	10.8	47	210
		Min.	12.5	0.3	0.1	0.5	0.7	10.8	46	210
		Ave.	12.6	0.4	0.1	0.5	0.8	10.8	46	210
Figs, SYP.P	1	...	...	...	...	...	...	...	...	...
		...	37.6	0.2	0.1	0.5	0.8	36.0	147	670

** Number of analyses unknown.

TABLE I *(Continued)*

Proximate Composition of Some Commercially Canned Foods

Canned Foods	No. of Analyses		Total Solids %	Ash %	Fat (E.E.) %	Protein (Nx6.25) %	Crude Fiber %	Carbohydrates by diff. %	Calories per 100 grams	Calories per pound
Fruit cocktail, WP	2	Max.	11.0	0.3	0.8	0.4	0.4	9.8	42	190
		Min.	8.8	0.2	0.1	0.3	0.4	7.0	36	160
		Ave.	9.9	0.3	0.4	0.4	0.4	8.4	39	180
Fruit cocktail, JP	1	...	...	...	...	...	...	...	...	...
		...	10.9	0.3	0.3	0.4	0.4	9.5	42	190
Fruit salad, WP	2	Max.	10.0	0.3	1.0	0.4	0.6	8.7	42	190
		Min.	9.7	0.2	0.1	0.3	0.3	7.8	37	170
		Ave.	9.9	0.3	0.6	0.4	0.5	8.3	39	180
Gooseberries, WP	**	...	...	...	...	...	...	...	...	...
		Ave.	7.0	0.3	0.2	0.5	1.5	4.5	28	130
Grapefruit, WP	4	Max.	10.0	0.4	0.5	0.8	0.2	8.6	39	180
		Min.	6.8	0.3	0.1	0.5	0.1	5.3	28	130
		Ave.	8.7	0.3	0.2	0.6	0.2	7.4	34	150
Grapefruit, JP	1	...	...	...	...	...	...	...	...	...
		...	10.2	0.3	0.1	0.6	0.1	9.0	39	180
Grapefruit, SYP.P	29	Max.	23.8	0.4	0.4	0.7	0.5	22.5	92	420
		Min.	15.9	0.3	0.03	0.5	0.1	14.5	62	280
		Ave.	19.8	0.4	0.1	0.6	0.2	18.5	77	350
Grapefruit juice, NS	58	Max.	13.1	0.8	0.3	0.6	0.1	12.0	54	240
		Min.	8.9	0.2	0.03	0.3	0.01	7.8	36	160
		Ave.	12.2	0.4	0.1	0.5	0.1	11.1	47	213
Grapefruit juice, AS	11	Max.	16.3	0.5	0.4	0.7	0.3	13.8	60	270
		Min.	10.8	0.3	trace	0.4	trace	9.9	43	200
		Ave.	13.8	0.5	0.1	0.5	0.1	12.4	53	240
Grapes, seedless, WP	1	...	...	...	...	...	...	...	...	...
		...	11.5	0.2	0.7	0.4	0.2	10.0	48	220
Ham, deviled	**	...	...	...	...	...	...	...	...	...
		Ave.	69.0	7.0	43.0	19.0	...	...	463	2100

** Number of analyses unknown.

TABLE I *(Continued)*

Proximate Composition of Some Commercially Canned Foods

Canned Foods	No. of Analyses		Total Solids %	Ash %	Fat (E.E.) %	Protein (Nx6.25) %	Crude Fiber %	Carbohydrates by diff. %	Calories per 100 grams	Calories per pound
Herring, plain	**	...	...	...	...	...	...	...	...	...
		...	...	...	...	...	...	...	...	...
		Ave.	36.9	3.9	12.4	20.7	...	...	194	880
Herring in tomato sauce	**	...	...	...	...	...	...	...	...	...
		...	...	...	...	...	...	...	...	...
		Ave.	33.3	3.3	10.5	15.8	...	...	172	780
Hominy	**	...	...	...	...	...	...	...	...	...
		...	...	...	...	...	...	...	...	...
		Ave.	17.4	0.5	0.2	1.8	0.1	14.8	68	310
Kraut	6	Max.	9.9	2.2	0.2	1.1	0.8	4.9	25	110
		Min.	6.6	1.7	0.2	0.9	0.6	3.1	18	80
		Ave.	7.6	2.0	0.2	1.0	0.7	3.8	21	100
Lamb, diced	1	...	...	...	...	...	...	...	...	...
		...	...	...	...	...	...	...	...	...
		...	25.7	1.4	6.3	18.2	...	...	131	590
Lamb, strained, SA	2	Max.	30.0	1.3	7.8	20.3	...	...	159	720
		Min.	21.0	1.0	4.5	15.6	...	...	103	470
		Ave.	25.5	1.2	6.2	18.0	...	...	131	590
Lemon juice	4	Max.	10.3	0.4	0.6	0.5	0.1	2.6	15	70
		Min.	8.6	0.2	0.1	0.4	trace	2.0	12	50
		Ave.	9.6	0.3	0.2	0.5	trace	2.3	13	60
Liver, beef, diced SA	1	...	...	...	...	...	...	...	...	...
		...	...	...	...	...	...	...	...	...
		...	29.8	1.7	4.3	21.6	...	...	125	570
Liver, beef, strained, SA	3	Max.	24.0	1.4	4.3	15.9	...	4.9	103	470
		Min.	21.3	1.0	3.5	14.2	...	1.8	100	450
		Ave.	22.4	1.2	3.8	15.0	...	2.2	102	460
Lobster	1	...	...	...	...	...	...	...	...	...
		...	...	...	...	...	...	...	...	...
		...	22.2	2.5	1.1	18.1	...	0.5	84	380
Loganberries, WP	1	...	...	...	...	...	...	...	...	...
		...	...	...	...	...	...	...	...	...
		...	10.8	0.4	0.6	1.0	2.0	6.8	37	170

** Number of analyses unknown.

TABLE I *(Continued)*

Proximate Composition of Some Commercially Canned Foods

Canned Foods	No. of Analyses		Total Solids %	Ash %	Fat (E.E.) %	Protein (Nx6.25) %	Crude Fiber %	Carbo-hy-drates by diff. %	Calories per 100 grams	Calories per pound
Loganberries, JP	1	...	...	...	...	...	...	...	...	...
		...	...	...	...	...	...	...	...	...
		...	13.3	0.4	0.1	0.8	2.1	9.9	43	200
Loganberry juice, NS	1	...	...	...	...	...	...	...	...	...
		...	...	...	...	...	...	...	...	...
		...	10.0	0.4	1.0	0.2	trace	8.4	43	200
Loganberry juice, AS	1	...	...	...	...	...	...	...	...	...
		...	...	...	...	...	...	...	...	...
		...	16.9	0.2	trace	0.2	trace	15.3	62	280
Mackerel	10	Max.	38.6	4.3	16.6	22.9	0.2	1.2	230	1040
		Min.	31.4	1.3	8.7	16.3	trace	trace	158	720
		Ave.	36.5	2.7	12.6	19.3	0.1	0.5	196	890
Meat, luncheon	1	...	...	...	...	...	...	...	...	...
		...	...	...	...	...	...	...	...	...
		...	43.7	...	22.5	15.2	...	1.7	270	1230
Milk, evap., NS	47	Max.	31.2	1.7	8.2	8.5	...	18.4	159	720
		Min.	25.5	1.1	6.3	7.0	...	8.5	135	610
		Ave.	26.2	1.5	7.9	7.2	...	9.9	138	630
Milk, evap., AS	5	Max.	74.0	1.9	9.1	8.6	...	56.7	334	1510
		Min.	63.0	1.5	8.0	7.6	...	53.0	324	1460
		Ave.	70.8	1.7	8.4	8.1	...	54.8	327	1490
Milk, skim	1	...	...	...	...	...	...	...	...	...
		...	...	...	...	...	...	...	...	...
		...	9.1	0.7	0.1	3.2	...	4.9	33	150
Milk, skim, evap.	1	...	...	...	...	...	...	...	...	...
		...	...	...	...	...	...	...	...	...
		...	20.0	2.0	0.3	7.3	...	10.4	74	340
Milk, whole	1	...	...	...	...	...	...	...	...	...
		...	...	...	...	...	...	...	...	...
		...	12.4	0.7	3.5	3.3	...	4.7	64	290
Mushrooms, WP	1	...	...	...	...	...	...	...	...	...
		...	...	...	...	...	...	...	...	...
		...	6.4	0.6	0.2	1.9	0.4	3.3	23	100

TABLE I *(Continued)*

Proximate Composition of Some Commercially Canned Foods

Canned Foods	No. of Analyses		Total Solids %	Ash %	Fat (E.E.) %	Protein (Nx6.25) %	Crude Fiber %	Carbohydrates by diff. %	Calories per 100 grams	Calories per pound
Mushrooms, BP	8	Max.	8.3	1.8	0.2	3.1	2.9	2.7	25	100
		Min.	6.2	1.5	0.1	2.6	0.6	0.4	14	60
		Ave.	7.1	1.6	0.2	2.9	0.9	1.5	19	90
Olives, ripe, BP	2	Max.	26.5	2.3	18.6	1.3	2.6	2.5	185	840
		Min.	17.5	2.1	9.1	1.3	1.8	2.4	97	440
		Ave.	22.0	2.2	13.9	1.3	2.2	2.5	141	640
Oranges, sliced, AS	1	...	...	...	...	...	...	...	...	...
		...	...	...	...	...	...	...	...	...
		...	16.8	0.5	0.2	0.9	0.5	14.7	64	290
Orange juice, NS	39	Max.	14.8	0.5	0.3	1.4	0.1	13.0	58	260
		Min.	10.5	0.4	trace	0.4	trace	9.4	41	190
		Ave.	12.4	0.5	0.2	0.9	0.03	10.7	48	220
Orange juice, AS	12	Max.	16.9	0.7	0.5	0.9	0.4	14.7	62	280
		Min.	13.3	0.1	0.1	0.4	trace	10.5	50	230
		Ave.	14.5	0.5	0.2	0.6	0.1	12.7	55	250
Orange and grapefruit juice, AS	3	Max.	16.0	0.5	0.1	0.6	0.1	14.0	59	270
		Min.	12.2	0.3	trace	0.4	trace	11.0	47	210
		Ave.	13.8	0.4	0.1	0.5	0.1	12.4	53	240
Oysters	1	...	...	...	...	...	...	...	...	...
		...	...	...	...	...	...	...	...	...
		...	16.6	1.5	2.4	8.8	...	3.9	72	330
Oysters, drained solids	**	...	...	...	...	...	...	...	...	...
		Ave.	19.7	2.0	2.0	9.8	...	5.9	81	370
Oysters, entire can contents	**	...	...	...	...	...	...	...	...	...
		Ave.	12.9	2.0	1.2	6.0	...	3.7	50	230
Peaches, WP	4	Max.	8.1	0.3	0.1	0.4	0.3	7.0	31	140
		Min.	6.9	0.2	0.1	0.2	0.2	5.8	25	110
		Ave.	7.3	0.3	0.1	0.3	0.2	6.4	27	120
Peaches, JP	3	Max.	13.6	0.5	0.5	0.5	0.4	11.8	54	240
		Min.	9.9	0.4	trace	0.3	0.2	8.7	38	170
		Ave.	11.5	0.4	0.2	0.4	0.3	10.1	44	200

** Number of analyses unknown.

TABLE I *(Continued)*

Proximate Composition of Some Commercially Canned Foods

Canned Foods	No. of Analyses		Total Solids %	Ash %	Fat (E.E.) %	Protein (Nx6.25) %	Crude Fiber %	Carbo-hy-drates by diff. %	Calories per 100 grams	Calories per pound
Peaches, cling, SYP.P	25	Max.	25.4	0.6	0.4	0.8	0.4	24.5	100	450
		Min.	14.5	0.2	trace	0.3	0.2	13.5	56	250
		Ave.	20.6	0.3	0.1	0.5	0.3	19.4	81	370
Peaches, freestone, SYP.P	20	Max.	29.0	0.5	0.2	0.8	0.5	27.7	113	510
		Min.	14.2	0.2	trace	0.2	0.2	12.9	55	250
		Ave.	22.1	0.3	0.1	0.5	0.4	20.8	86	390
Peaches, chopped AS	1	...	...	...	...	...	...	...	...	...
		...	...	...	...	...	...	...	...	...
		...	16.3	0.4	trace	0.5	0.6	14.8	61	280
Peaches, strained NS, NSA	3	Max.	15.2	0.6	0.1	0.5	0.9	13.6	58	260
		Min.	12.6	0.3	0.01	0.4	0.3	10.0	44	200
		Ave.	14.1	0.4	0.1	0.4	0.6	12.3	53	240
Peaches, strained AS	1	...	...	...	...	...	...	...	...	...
		...	...	...	...	...	...	...	...	...
		...	22.3	0.2	0.2	0.4	0.5	20.5	85	390
Peach juice, NS	1	...	...	...	...	...	...	...	...	...
		...	...	...	...	...	...	...	...	...
		...	11.3	0.4	0.4	0.4	trace	10.1	46	210
Pear juice, NS	1	...	...	...	...	...	...	...	...	...
		...	...	...	...	...	...	...	...	...
		...	12.4	0.3	0.5	0.3	trace	11.3	51	230
Pears, Bartlett, WP	3	Max.	9.7	0.2	0.2	0.3	1.1	8.5	36	160
		Min.	7.9	0.2	0.1	0.2	0.6	6.1	27	120
		Ave.	8.8	0.2	0.1	0.2	0.8	7.5	32	140
Pears, Bartlett, JP	2	Max.	13.0	0.3	0.1	0.2	0.7	11.9	49	220
		Min.	12.4	0.3	0.1	0.2	0.5	11.6	48	220
		Ave.	12.7	0.3	0.1	0.2	0.6	11.8	49	220
Pears, Bartlett, SYP.P	39	Max.	23.2	0.3	0.3	0.5	0.9	22.5	91	410
		Min.	13.8	0.1	0.1	0.2	0.1	16.1	67	300
		Ave.	19.6	0.2	0.1	0.3	0.6	18.6	77	350
Pears, chopped, AS	2	Max.	17.1	0.3	0.1	0.3	1.3	15.3	63	290
		Min.	16.3	0.2	trace	0.3	1.2	14.4	58	260
		Ave.	16.7	0.2	0.1	0.3	1.2	14.9	61	280

TABLE I *(Continued)*

Proximate Composition of Some Commercially Canned Foods

Canned Foods	No. of Analyses		Total Solids %	Ash %	Fat (E.E.) %	Protein (Nx6.25) %	Crude Fiber %	Carbo-hy-drates by diff. %	Calories per 100 grams	Calories per pound
Pears, strained	2	Max.	16.8	0.3	0.1	0.6	1.2	15.2	61	280
		Min.	15.6	0.2	0.02	0.2	1.0	13.7	57	260
		Ave.	16.2	0.2	0.1	0.4	1.1	14.5	59	270
Peas, WP	2	Max.	12.4	0.4	0.4	3.7	1.2	6.8	45	200
		Min.	11.3	0.4	0.2	3.1	0.8	6.7	41	190
		Ave.	11.9	0.4	0.3	3.4	1.0	6.8	43	200
Peas, Alaska, SA	37	Max.	21.1	1.6	0.4	4.6	2.1	14.3	77	350
		Min.	13.1	0.8	0.1	2.3	1.0	7.0	45	200
		Ave.	17.4	1.1	0.3	3.5	1.5	11.1	61	280
Peas and carrots, BP	1	...	...	...	...	...	...	...	...	...
		...	11.3	1.3	0.1	2.3	1.2	6.4	36	160
Peas, strained, SA	6	Max.	16.1	1.1	0.4	4.6	1.8	9.9	59	270
		Min.	13.4	0.5	0.1	3.5	0.8	7.6	47	210
		Ave.	14.4	1.0	0.3	3.7	1.0	8.4	51	230
Peas, strained, NS, NSA	7	Max.	17.2	0.7	0.5	4.9	1.7	9.8	62	280
		Min.	12.7	0.4	0.3	3.2	0.4	7.1	49	220
		Ave.	14.4	0.5	0.4	4.2	0.7	8.5	55	250
Peas, sweet, SA	151	Max.	20.9	1.6	0.8	4.8	2.0	13.6	74	340
		Min.	11.7	0.7	0.1	2.3	1.0	6.2	40	180
		Ave.	15.3	1.1	0.4	3.4	1.4	9.0	53	240
Peppers	2	Max.	10.0	1.6	0.4	1.0	0.7	7.3	37	170
		Min.	7.9	0.6	0.3	0.7	0.5	4.8	25	110
		Ave.	9.0	1.1	0.4	0.9	0.6	6.1	31	140
Pimientos, no added water	1	...	...	...	...	...	...	...	...	...
		...	7.7	0.4	0.7	1.0	0.5	5.1	31	140
Pimientos, BP	4	Max.	8.5	0.5	0.5	1.0	0.9	6.2	31	140
		Min.	5.5	0.3	0.3	0.8	0.5	3.2	19	90
		Ave.	7.1	0.4	0.3	0.9	0.7	4.8	26	120
Pineapple, crushed, JP	4	Max.	16.9	0.5	0.1	0.6	0.6	15.6	65	290
		Min.	14.5	0.3	trace	0.5	0.4	12.6	53	240
		Ave.	15.9	0.4	trace	0.6	0.5	14.2	60	270

TABLE I *(Continued)*

Proximate Composition of Some Commercially Canned Foods

Canned Foods	No. of Analyses		Total Solids %	Ash %	Fat (E.E.) %	Protein (Nx6.25) %	Crude Fiber %	Carbohydrates by diff. %	Calories per 100 grams	Calories per pound
Pineapple, crushed, JP, AS	2	Max.	25.2	0.4	0.1	0.5	0.4	22.7	94	430
		Min.	21.8	0.4	0.1	0.4	0.4	19.5	81	370
		Ave.	23.5	0.4	0.1	0.5	0.4	21.1	87	390
Pineapple, crushed, AS	4	Max.	25.9	0.5	0.1	1.0	0.3	24.3	102	460
		Min.	16.6	0.3	0.1	0.3	0.1	14.5	60	270
		Ave	21.0	0.4	0.1	0.6	0.2	19.2	81	370
Pineapple, sliced, WP	3	Max.	14.4	0.4	0.1	0.3	0.3	13.4	55	250
		Min.	12.0	0.3	trace	0.3	0.2	11.2	46	210
		Ave.	13.3	0.4	0.1	0.3	0.3	12.0	50	230
Pineapple, sliced, JP	4	Max.	16.5	0.5	0.1	0.5	0.6	15.2	63	290
		Min.	15.1	0.4	trace	0.3	0.3	12.6	53	240
		Ave.	16.1	0.4	0.1	0.4	0.4	14.4	60	270
Pineapple, sliced, AS	26	Max.	28.7	0.7	0.4	1.0	0.4	27.5	114	520
		Min.	16.6	0.2	0.01	0.3	0.1	14.5	60	270
		Ave.	24.7	0.4	0.2	0.4	0.3	23.3	96	440
Pineapple juice, NS	24	Max.	17.5	0.5	0.3	0.6	0.2	15.9	66	300
		Min.	12.9	0.3	trace	0.3	trace	11.1	46	210
		Ave.	15.1	0.4	0.1	0.4	0.1	13.9	58	260
Purple plums (prunes), WP	1	...	...	...	...	...	...	...	...	...
		...	...	...	...	...	...	...	...	...
		...	10.6	0.3	0.1	0.5	0.2	9.5	41	190
Purple Plums (prunes), JP	1	...	...	...	...	...	...	...	...	...
		...	...	...	...	...	...	...	...	...
		...	20.1	0.6	0.1	0.5	0.2	18.7	78	350
Purple Plums (prunes), SYP.P, EP	18	Max.	27.3	0.6	0.3	0.6	0.8	25.3	105	480
		Min.	21.4	0.3	0.1	0.3	0.2	20.2	83	380
		Ave.	23.9	0.5	0.1	0.4	0.3	22.5	93	420
Plum juice, NS	1	...	...	...	...	...	...	...	...	...
		...	...	...	...	...	...	...	...	...
		...	14.2	0.3	0.5	0.3	0.1	13.0	58	260
Pork, diced, SA	1	...	...	...	...	...	...	...	...	...
		...	...	...	...	...	...	...	...	...
		...	29.3	1.5	6.5	21.8	...	...	145	660

TABLE I *(Continued)*

Proximate Composition of Some Commercially Canned Foods

Canned Foods	No. of Analyses		Total Solids %	Ash %	Fat (E.E.) %	Protein (Nx6.25) %	Crude Fiber %	Carbohydrates by diff. %	Calories per 100 grams	Calories per pound
Pork, strained, SA	1	...	...	...	...	...	...	...	...	...
		...	...	...	...	...	...	...	...	...
		...	24.1	1.2	6.0	17.1	...	...	122	550
Pork sausage, bulk	**	...	...	...	...	...	...	...	...	...
		...	...	...	...	...	...	...	...	...
		Ave.	43.0	...	24.0	16.0	...	...	280	1270
Prunes, WP	1	...	...	...	...	...	...	...	...	...
		...	...	...	...	...	...	...	...	...
		...	38.4	1.1	0.1	1.3	0.7	35.2	147	670
Prunes, chopped	1	...	...	...	...	...	...	...	...	...
		...	...	...	...	...	...	...	...	...
		...	28.5	0.7	1.9	0.7	0.6	24.6	118	530
Prunes, strained, NS	7	Max.	34.3	0.9	1.2	1.8	2.0	31.4	134	610
		Min.	21.0	0.7	trace	0.7	0.6	16.4	79	360
		Ave.	29.9	0.8	0.4	1.1	1.0	26.4	114	520
Prune juice	**	...	...	...	...	...	...	...	...	...
		...	...	...	...	...	...	...	...	...
		Ave.	20.0	0.3	trace	0.4	...	19.3	78	350
Pumpkin	**	...	...	...	...	...	...	...	...	...
		...	...	...	...	...	...	...	...	...
		Ave.	9.8	...	0.3	1.0	...	7.9	38	170
Raspberries, black WP	2	Max.	15.1	0.6	1.1	1.1	3.3	9.0	51	230
		Min.	11.4	0.2	1.1	1.1	3.2	5.8	38	170
		Ave.	13.3	0.4	1.1	1.1	3.3	7.4	44	200
Raspberries, red, WP	1	...	...	...	...	...	...	...	...	...
		...	...	...	...	...	...	...	...	...
		...	11.8	0.5	0.9	0.8	2.1	7.5	41	190
Raspberries, red, JP	2	Max.	15.1	0.5	1.2	1.0	2.5	11.4	52	240
		Min.	14.4	0.4	0.1	0.7	2.3	9.4	49	220
		Ave.	14.8	0.5	0.7	0.9	2.4	10.4	51	230
Raspberry juice, red, NS	1	...	...	...	...	...	...	...	...	...
		...	...	...	...	...	...	...	...	...
		...	9.4	0.4	0.1	0.3	trace	8.6	37	170

** Number of analyses unknown.

TABLE I (*Continued*)

Proximate Composition of Some Commercially Canned Foods

Canned Foods	No. of Analyses		Total Solids %	Ash %	Fat (E.E.) %	Protein (Nx6.25) %	Crude Fiber %	Carbo-hy-drates by diff. %	Calories per 100 grams	Calories per pound
Rhubarb, WP	1	...	...	...	...	...	...	...	...	...
		...	...	...	...	...	...	...	...	...
		...	5.2	0.7	0.7	0.5	1.0	2.3	18	80
Salmon	16	Max.	36.8	3.1	15.7	21.7	0.2	2.1	212	960
		Min.	29.3	0.8	4.9	17.7	0.02	...	131	590
		Ave.	32.5	1.7	8.9	20.7	...	...	162	740
Sardines in oil	10	Max.	54.1	5.1	31.1	23.2	0.2	1.0	358	1620
		Min.	41.5	2.9	18.6	17.5	0.02	0.4	244	1110
		Ave.	44.8	3.8	22.1	19.5	0.1	0.5	280	1270
Sardines in mustard sauce	**	...	...	...	...	...	...	...	...	...
		...	...	...	...	...	...	...	...	...
		Ave.	37.5	3.5	11.8	20.0	...	2.2	195	890
Sardines in tomato sauce	17	Max.	41.3	3.9	20.6	20.5	0.4	3.2	258	1170
		Min.	29.4	2.0	5.6	16.9	0.1	0.6	123	560
		Ave.	36.6	2.8	14.2	17.7	0.2	1.5	205	930
Shrimp, dry pack	4	Max.	37.1	6.5	1.5	28.8	0.2	0.8	129	590
		Min.	30.2	2.9	0.8	25.5	0.1	0.2	109	490
		Ave.	33.3	4.5	1.2	26.4	0.1	0.4	117	530
Shrimp, wet pack	6	Max.	24.3	6.2	0.8	20.0	0.1	1.5	85	390
		Min.	19.9	1.9	0.5	13.8	0.04	0.02	67	300
		Ave.	21.9	4.7	0.7	15.6	0.1	0.4	72	330
Spinach, WP	4	Max.	9.1	1.2	0.5	3.5	1.0	3.3	29	130
		Min.	6.6	0.7	0.3	2.1	0.8	2.4	22	100
		Ave.	7.9	0.9	0.4	2.9	0.9	2.9	26	120
Spinach, SA	55	Max.	9.2	2.2	0.6	3.2	1.0	4.1	32	150
		Min.	4.8	1.1	0.3	1.3	0.5	1.3	15	70
		Ave.	7.0	1.6	0.4	2.0	0.7	2.3	21	100
Spinach, chopped, NSA	1	...	...	...	...	...	...	...	...	...
		...	...	...	...	...	...	...	...	...
		...	5.5	1.1	0.2	1.8	0.7	1.7	16	70
Spinach, chopped, SA	4	Max.	6.1	1.8	0.5	1.8	0.9	2.0	17	80
		Min.	5.6	1.3	0.2	1.1	0.3	1.5	15	70
		Ave.	5.8	1.5	0.4	1.5	0.6	1.9	16	70

** Number of analyses unknown.

TABLE I *(Continued)*

Proximate Composition of Some Commercially Canned Foods

Canned Foods	No. of Analyses		Total Solids %	Ash %	Fat (E.E.) %	Protein (Nx6.25) %	Crude Fiber %	Carbohydrates by diff. %	Calories per 100 grams	Calories per pound
Spinach, strained, NSA	6	Max.	7.3	1.6	0.5	2.4	0.7	2.8	24	110
		Min.	.6	0.8	0.2	1.6	0.4	1.3	15	70
		Ave.	6.1	1.2	0.4	1.9	0.5	2.0	19	90
Spinach, strained, SA	7	Max.	7.3	1.7	0.4	2.3	1.1	2.4	21	100
		Min.	4.6	1.2	0.3	1.2	0.4	0.9	13	60
		Ave.	6.2	1.5	0.3	1.8	0.7	1.8	17	80
Squash	**	...	...	...	...	...	...	...	...	...
		...	...	...	...	...	...	...	...	...
		A e.	9.8	0.6	0.3	1.0	1.2	6.7	39	180
Strawberries, WP	1	...	...	...	...	...	...	...	...	...
		...	...	...	...	...	...	...	...	...
		...	.9	0.5	0.6	0.9	1.3	5.6	32	150
Strawberries, JP	2	Max.	12.5	0.5	0.8	1.0	0.9	10.7	45	200
		Min.	10.2	0.4	trace	0.6	0.7	7.1	40	180
		Ave.	11.4	0.5	0.4	0.8	0.8	8.9	43	190
Strawberries, SYP.P	**	...	...	...	...	...	...	...	...	...
		...	...	...	...	...	...	...	...	...
		Ave.	29.2	0.5	0.2	0.5	0.7	27.3	116	520
Sweetpotatoes	5	Max.	32.1	1.0	1.0	2.1	1.2	28.5	120	540
		Min.	27.5	0.8	0.1	1.1	1.0	24.3	103	470
		Ave.	29.1	0.9	0.1	1.5	1.0	25.7	110	490
Tomatoes, SA, JP	86	Max.	7.6	1.1	0.6	1.3	0.6	5.4	26	120
		Min.	4.9	0.4	0.1	0.6	0.2	2.4	15	70
		Ave.	6.3	0.8	0.2	1.0	0.4	4.0	21	100
Tomatoes, strained, NS, NSA	7	Max.	14.2	1.1	0.3	2.5	0.6	9.9	51	230
		Min.	4.6	0.4	trace	0.8	0.2	3.2	16	70
		Ave.	10.4	0.8	0.2	1.7	0.4	7.2	37	170
Tomatoes, strained	1	...	...	...	...	...	...	...	...	...
		...	...	...	...	...	...	...	...	...
		...	6.5	0.1	0.1	1.1	0.3	4.9	21	100
Tomatoes, strained, SA	4	Max.	11.2	1.2	0.3	1.9	0.6	7.4	38	170
		Min.	6.4	0.8	0.1	0.9	0.2	4.2	23	100
		Ave.	7.9	1.0	0.2	1.3	0.4	5.2	27	120

** Number of analyses unknown.

TABLE I *(Concluded)*

Proximate Composition of Some Commercially Canned Foods

Canned Foods	No. of Analyses		Total Solids %	Ash %	Fat (E.E.) %	Protein (Nx6.25) %	Crude Fiber %	Carbo-hy-drates by diff. %	Calories per 100 grams	Calories per pound
Tomato juice, NSA	2	Max.	6.7	0.5	0.3	1.1	0.2	4.3	22	100
		Min.	5.6	0.4	0.1	1.0	0.2	3.7	22	100
		Ave.	6.2	0.5	0.2	1.1	0.2	4.0	22	100
Tomato juice, SA	164	Max.	9.0	1.6	0.3	1.5	0.3	6.8	31	140
		Min.	4.8	0.7	0.03	0.5	0.02	2.4	14	60
		Ave.	6.3	1.1	0.1	0.9	0.2	4.0	21	100
Tomato paste	**	...	...	...	...	...	...	...	...	...
		...	...	...	...	...	...	...	...	...
		Ave.	28.3	3.3	1.4	4.7	0.9	17.8	110	480
Tomato puree	**	...	...	...	...	...	...	...	...	...
		...	...	...	...	...	...	...	...	...
		Ave.	10.8	1.3	0.5	1.8	0.4	6.8	40	185
Tuna	9	Max.	49.2	3.0	22.4	27.7	0.5	1.7	295	1340
		Min.	41.1	0.9	11.6	22.4	0.02	0.1	215	980
		Ave.	45.0	1.8	17.7	24.4	...	...	261	1180
Turnip greens	6	Max.	7.6	1.6	0.4	2.1	0.8	3.3	23	100
		Min.	4.5	1.0	0.3	1.1	0.6	1.3	12	50
		Ave.	6.3	1.3	0.3	1.5	0.7	2.5	19	90

** Number of analyses unknown.

TABLE II

Calicum, Phosphorus, and Iron Contents of Canned Foods *

After Kramer (1946)

Canned Foods	No. of Samples		Content in milligrams per 100 grams		
			Calcium	Phosphorus	Iron
Apricots	26	Max.	10	20	3.0
		Min.	7	13	0.3
		Ave.	8	16	0.7
Asparagus, green	40	Max.	26	68	7.7
		Min.	10	30	0.2
		Ave.	18	43	1.7
Asparagus, white	16	Max.	20	46	3.7
		Min.	10	20	0.2
		Ave.	15	33	0.9
Beans, baked	5	Max.	63	135	4.1
		Min.	48	80	1.3
		Ave.	56	106	2.6
Beans, green, cut	112	Max.	56	46	4.7
		Min.	18	10	0.2
		Ave.	34	21	1.2
Beans, Lima, green	53	Max.	41	98	3.8
		Min.	19	42	1.4
		Ave.	26	67	2.4
Beets	47	Max.	23	44	10.9
		Min.	10	6	0.3
		Ave.	14	17	1.8
Blackberries	6	Max.	20	23	5.0
		Min.	14	15	1.0
		Ave.	18	19	2.6
Blueberries	6	Max.	13	8	6.8
		Min.	9	4	1.9
		Ave.	11	6	5.1
Carrots	39	Max.	30	30	2.8
		Min.	15	10	0.2
		Ave.	25	20	0.7
Cherries, red, sour, pitted	4	Max.	12	13	3.4
		Min.	11	12	2.3
		Ave.	11	12	2.8
Corn, white, cream style	11	Max.	4	70	0.7
		Min.	1	41	0.4
		Ave.	2	55	0.6
Corn, white, whole grain	76	Max.	7	58	0.9
		Min.	2	30	0.2
		Ave.	5	45	0.5

* Based on entire contents of can, unless otherwise noted.

TABLE II *(Continued)*

Calcium, Phosphorus, and Iron Contents of Canned Foods *

After Kramer: (1946)

Canned Foods	No. of Samples		Content in milligrams per 100 grams		
			Calcium	Phosphorus	Iron
Corn, yellow cream style	25	Max.	9	78	0.9
		Min.	1	37	0.4
		Ave.	3	57	0.6
Corn, yellow whole grain	114	Max.	11	79	0.9
		Min.	1	36	0.1
		Ave.	4	50	0.4
Corn, yellow vacuum pack	6	Max.	4	79	0.7
		Min.	2	67	0.5
		Ave.	3	73	0.5
Grapefruit juice	54	Max.	16	16	1.5
		Min.	5	8	0.1
		Ave.	8	13	0.4
Grapefruit segments	29	Max.	18	18	0.7
		Min.	9	9	0.2
		Ave.	13	14	0.3
Kraut	6	Max.	42	21	10.1
		Min.	30	16	3.5
		Ave.	36	18	6.9
Mackerel	7	Max.	284	407	2.4
		Min.	151	210	1.6
		Ave.	225	274	1.9
Mushrooms	5	Max.	7	76	0.8
		Min.	5	62	0.3
		Ave.	6	68	0.5
Orange juice	36	Max.	13	25	2.4
		Min.	6	11	0.1
		Ave.	10	19	0.5
Peaches, cling	25	Max.	6	14	0.8
		Min.	2	8	0.1
		Ave.	3	11	0.3
Peaches, freestone	20	Max.	5	16	0.7
		Min.	3	9	0.1
		Ave.	4	12	0.3
Pears	44	Max.	9	12	1.0
		Min.	4	4	0.2
		Ave.	6	7	0.5
Peas, Alaska	37	Max.	29	89	3.0
		Min.	14	31	0.6
		Ave.	20	66	1.7

* Based on entire contents of can, unless otherwise noted.

TABLE II *(Continued)*

Calcium, Phosphorus, and Iron Contents of Canned Foods *

After Kramer: (1946)

Canned Foods	No. of Samples		Content in milligrams per 100 grams		
			Calcium	Phosphorus	Iron
Peas, sweet	150	Max.	34	92	4.4
		Min.	11	32	0.5
		Ave.	19	58	1.5
Peppers	2	Max.	9	21	1.9
		Min.	7	16	1.7
		Ave.	8	19	1.8
Pimientos	3	Max.	7	16	1.6
		Min.	6	14	0.9
		Ave.	6	15	1.3
Pineapple juice	17	Max.	23	13	0.7
		Min.	10	6	0.1
		Ave.	15	9	0.3
Pineapple, sliced	17	Max.	43	12	2.9
		Min.	10	5	0.3
		Ave.	20	8	0.7
Plums, purple (prunes) Edible portion only	15	Max.	11	16	2.4
		Min.	7	10	0.4
		Ave.	8	13	1.0
Salmon	5	Max.	245	328	0.9
		Min.	148	267	0.4
		Ave.	184	292	0.6
Sardines in oil	9	Max.	447	494	7.8
		Min.	296	366	1.4
		Ave.	354	434	3.5
Sardines in tomato sauce	16	Max.	484	425	7.0
		Min.	300	305	1.5
		Ave.	381	168	4.1
Shrimp, dry pack	3	Max.	110	263	4.2
		Min.	92	209	3.2
		Ave.	104	240	3.5
Shrimp, wet pack	5	Max.	63	160	2.8
		Min.	43	135	1.6
		Ave.	55	149	2.2
Spinach	55	Max.	163	44	10.9
		Min.	43	11	0.8
		Ave.	85	26	2.1
Sweetpotatoes	5	Max.	31	56	0.7
		Min.	17	36	0.4
		Ave.	21	50	0.6

* Based on entire contents of can, unless otherwise noted.

TABLE II *(Concluded)*

Calcium, Phosphorus, and Iron Contents of Canned Foods *
After Kramer: (1946)

Canned Foods	No. of Samples		Content in milligrams per 100 grams		
			Calcium	Phosphorus	Iron
Tomatoes	84	Max.	8†	30	2.0
		Min.	4†	12	0.2
		Ave.	6†	19	0.5
Tomato juice	138	Max.	11	26	8.0
		Min.	3	12	0.2
		Ave.	7	18	0.9
Turnip greens	6	Max.	136	40	7.3
		Min.	74	24	2.9
		Ave.	100	30	4.6
Tuna	6	Max.	8	253	2.3
		Min.	8	210	0.7
		Ave.	8	224	1.2

* Based on entire contents of can, unless otherwise noted.

† Represents 56 samples with no calcium added; for 28 samples with added calcium: Max. = 32, Min. = 22, Ave. = 28.

TABLE III

Carotene, Ascorbic Acid, Thiamine, Riboflavin, Niacin, and Pantothenic Acid Contents of Selected Canned Foods

Adapted from: Pressley et al. (1944), Ives et al. (1944), Thompson et al. (1944), Ives et al. (1945), Hinman et al. (1947), and Neilands et al. (1947)*

Canned Foods	No. of Samples †		Carotene	Ascorbic Acid	Thiamine	Riboflavin	Niacin	Pantothenic Acid ‡
			Content in milligrams per 100 grams					
Apricots	26	Max.	1.74	5.7	0.026	0.039	0.48	0.20
		Min.	0.93	1.1	0.008	0.010	0.18	0.04
		Ave.	1.29	3.9	0.018	0.022	0.35	0.09
Asparagus, green	42	Max.	0.50	25.3	0.122	0.190	1.19	0.43
		Min.	0.16	5.4	0.040	0.039	0.22	0.07
		Ave.	0.30	15.3	0.064	0.094	0.82	0.19
Asparagus, white	16	Max.	0.06	18.1	0.055	0.073	0.88	0.19
		Min.	trace	11.6	0.043	0.044	0.55	0.09
		Ave.	0.03	15.0	0.049	0.057	0.71	0.13
Beans, baked	5	Max.	0.06	4.3	0.053	0.059	1.10	0.11
		Min.	trace	1.8	0.015	0.019	0.15	0.06
		Ave.	0.03	2.8	0.034	0.042	0.51	0.09
Beans, green, cut	96	Max.	0.34	7.3	0.053	0.065	0.60	0.14
		Min.	0.08	0.6	0.011	0.018	0.11	0.02
		Ave.	0.18	3.3	0.029	0.035	0.32	0.06
Beans, Lima, green	53	Max.	0.27	12.1	0.048	0.062	0.83	0.21
		Min.	0.03	1.3	0.019	0.022	0.11	0.03
		Ave.	0.07	7.2	0.032	0.040	0.54	0.11
Beets	41	Max.	0.05	7.0	0.015	0.059	0.43	0.19
		Min.	trace	trace	0.004	0.011	0.06	0.04
		Ave.	0.01	3.0	0.009	0.024	0.14	0.08
Blackberries	6	Max.	0.13	8.1	0.016	0.022	0.25	0.09
		Min.	0.08	4.3	0.009	0.018	0.17	0.07
		Ave.	0.11	6.2	0.013	0.019	0.21	0.08
Blueberries	5	Max.	0.03	22.4	0.018	0.015	0.23	0.10
		Min.	0.02	7.8	0.010	0.012	0.16	0.05
		Ave.	0.02	13.3	0.014	0.014	0.19	0.07
Carrots	33	Max.	11.35	4.6	0.028	0.042	0.50	0.21
		Min.	3.86	1.0	0.013	0.009	0.19	0.04
		Ave.	7.35	2.1	0.022	0.021	0.35	0.13
Cherries red, sour, pitted	4	Max.	0.63	9.1	0.028	0.020	0.21	0.22
		Min.	0.43	4.1	0.024	0.014	0.17	0.02
		Ave.	0.52	5.9	0.027	0.016	0.19	0.12

* For complete reference, see Selected Bibliography, beginning page 245.
† In some instances all samples of a given product were not analyzed for all vitamin factors.
‡ Determined as calcium pantothenate. The relationship of pantothenic acid to human nutrition has not been established.

TABLE III *(Continued)*

Carotene, Ascorbic Acid, Thiamine, Riboflavin, Niacin, and Pantothenic Acid Contents of Selected Canned Foods

Canned Foods	No. of Samples †		Carotene	Ascorbic Acid	Thia-mine	Ribo-flavin	Niacin	Panto-thenic Acid ‡
Corn, white,	12	Max.	0.02	8.0	0.038	0.054	1.50	0.26
cream style		Min.	0.01	2.4	0.018	0.043	0.77	0.14
		Ave.	0.01	5.5	0.027	0.049	1.09	0.21
Corn, yellow	20	Max.	0.17	7.6	0.044	0.058	1.30	0.32
cream style		Min.	0.04	2.7	0.019	0.041	0.50	0.10
		Ave.	0.08	5.6	0.030	0.052	0.95	0.21
Corn, white,	78	Max.	0.11	6.6	0.039	0.064	1.50	0.50
whole grain		Min.	trace	2.0	0.010	0.027	0.46	0.10
		Ave.	0.02	4.7	0.021	0.044	0.93	0.19
Corn, yellow,	118	Max.	0.16	9.0	0.045	0.072	1.30	0.32
whole grain		Min.	0.04	1.3	0.013	0.025	0.44	0.09
		Ave.	0.08	4.5	0.026	0.045	0.83	0.21
Grapefruit juice	54	Max.	0.02	44.7	0.051	0.033	0.47	0.26
		Min.	trace	26.3	0.012	0.005	0.07	0.07
		Ave.	0.01	33.2	0.028	0.017	0.17	0.12
Grapefruit	29	Max.	0.02	32.3	0.046	0.039	0.35	0.19
segments		Min.	trace	20.3	0.007	0.008	0.13	0.06
		Ave.	0.01	24.8	0.029	0.020	0.21	0.13
Kraut	6	Max.	0.04	24.2	0.043	0.068	0.13	0.11
		Min.	0.02	12.4	0.028	0.032	0.09	0.08
		Ave.	0.03	17.6	0.034	0.042	0.11	0.09
Mackerel	18	Max.	§	...	0.086	0.380	11.40	0.54
		Min.	§	...	0.018	0.130	4.01	0.13
		Ave.	§	...	0.037	0.236	7.62	0.31
Mushrooms	5	Max.	0.01	2.0	0.019	0.240	1.90	1.10
		Min.	trace	1.6	0.012	0.150	1.40	0.68
		Ave.	0.01	1.7	0.016	0.194	1.63	0.93
Orange juice	36	Max.	0.22	52.4	0.103	0.038	0.30	0.20
		Min.	0.01	11.1	0.033	0.012	0.17	0.06
		Ave.	0.10	35.0	0.073	0.020	0.24	0.13
Peaches, cling	26	Max.	0.51	5.8	0.011	0.030	1.18	0.07
		Min.	0.17	2.0	0.005	0.013	0.22	0.02
		Ave.	0.26	3.8	0.007	0.021	0.60	0.04
Peaches,	19	Max.	0.39	3.7	0.011	0.034	0.90	0.13
freestone		Min.	0.09	1.4	0.005	0.009	0.29	0.02
		Ave.	0.20	2.5	0.008	0.020	0.55	0.06

† In some instances all samples of a given product were not analyzed for all vitamin factors.

‡ Determined as calcium pantothenate. The relationship of pantothenic acid to human nutrition has not been established.

§ See Table V for vitamin A values of fish products.

TABLE III *(Continued)*

Carotene, Ascorbic Acid, Thiamine, Riboflavin, Niacin, and Pantothenic Acid Contents of Selected Canned Foods

				Content in milligrams per 100 grams				
Canned Foods	No. of Samples †		Carotene	Ascorbic Acid	Thiamine	Riboflavin	Niacin	Pantothenic Acid ‡
Pears	43	Max.	0.01	2.5	0.012	0.032	0.46	0.04
		Min.	trace	trace	0.005	0.009	0.06	0.01
		Ave.	trace	1.5	0.009	0.018	0.14	0.02
Peas	209	Max.	0.51	14.1	0.188	0.100	2.69	0.27
		Min.	0.15	3.1	0.042	0.025	0.42	0.07
		Ave.	0.27	9.3	0.109	0.056	0.99	0.15
Peppers	2	Max.	2.44	131.0	0.048	0.082	0.95	0.12
		Min.	1.54	107.1	0.033	0.080	0.45	0.09
		Ave.	1.99	119.0	0.039	0.081	0.70	0.10
Pimientos	3	Max.	2.24	150.0	0.030	. . .	. . .	. . .
		Min.	0.68	80.0	0.020	. . .	. . .	. . .
		Ave.	1.38	113.0	0.025	0.065	0.38	0.18
Pineapple juice	18	Max.	0.04	14.2	0.070	0.031	0.20	0.18
		Min.	0.01	3.2	0.031	0.004	0.16	0.07
		Ave.	0.03	8.5	0.053	0.018	0.18	0.10
Pineapple, sliced	17	Max.	0.04	7.0	0.087	0.030	0.23	0.15
		Min.	0.01	0.8	0.053	0.006	0.12	0.05
		Ave.	0.03	5.1	0.071	0.021	0.17	0.10
Plums, purple (prunes) Edible portion only	18	Max.	1.16	3.4	0.039	0.032	0.49	0.11
		Min.	0.44	trace	0.016	0.011	0.19	0.03
		Ave.	0.72	1.6	0.023	0.020	0.36	0.07
Salmon	16	Max.	§	. . .	0.052	0.200	8.91	0.73
		Min.	§	. . .	0.014	0.110	5.95	0.47
		Ave.	§	. . .	0.027	0.160	7.53	0.58
Sardines in brine	6	Max.	§	. . .	0.019	0.370	8.80	0.83
		Min.	§	. . .	trace	0.230	6.20	0.49
		Ave.	§	. . .	0.007	0.300	7.40	0.60
Sardines in oil (oil removed)	19	Max.	§	. . .	0.042	0.230	7.15	0.65
		Min.	§	. . .	0.003	0.090	2.92	0.20
		Ave.	§	. . .	0.018	0.163	4.75	0.43
Sardines in tomato sauce	21	Max.	§	. . .	0.017	0.380	8.30	0.59
		Min.	§	. . .	0.006	0.120	2.36	0.12
		Ave.	§	. . .	0.010	0.247	5.01	0.44
Shrimp, dry pack	3	Max.	. . .	. . .	0.011	0.037	3.40	0.35
		Min.	. . .	. . .	0.006	0.027	1.10	0.26
		Ave.	. . .	. . .	0.009	0.032	2.23	0.29

† In some instances all samples of a given product were not analyzed for all vitamin factors.

‡ Determined as calcium pantothenate. The relationship of pantothenic acid to human nutrition has not been established.

§ See Table V for vitamin A values of fish products.

TABLE III *(Concluded)*
Carotene, Ascorbic Acid, Thiamine, Riboflavin, Niacin, and Pantothenic Acid Contents of Selected Canned Foods

Canned Foods	No. of Samples †		Carotene	Ascorbic Acid	Thiamine	Riboflavin	Niacin	Pantothenic Acid ‡
			Content in milligrams per 100 grams					
Shrimp, wet pack	5	Max.	...	...	0.011	0.035	2.52	0.22
(liquid removed)		Min.	...	...	0.004	0.026	0.72	0.18
		Ave.	...	...	0.008	0.031	1.36	0.21
Spinach	56	Max.	4.81	35.1	0.041	0.150	0.64	0.14
		Min.	1.68	3.4	0.007	0.024	0.15	0.02
		Ave.	3.29	13.1	0.019	0.098	0.32	0.05
Sweetpotatoes	5	Max.	7.99	19.3	0.061	0.051	0.80	0.49
		Min.	2.36	14.4	0.042	0.037	0.26	0.37
		Ave.	5.94	16.2	0.053	0.043	0.49	0.42
Tomatoes	84	Max.	0.96	27.1	0.084	0.050	0.99	0.44
		Min.	0.35	9.5	0.019	0.011	0.41	0.11
		Ave.	0.58	17.0	0.052	0.027	0.69	0.23
Tomato juice	140	Max.	0.96	30.0	0.094	0.046	1.77	0.39
		Min.	0.16	2.5	0.014	0.009	0.42	0.17
		Ave.	0.51	14.4	0.053	0.027	0.78	0.25
Turnip greens	6	Max.	4.63	23.6	0.023	0.110	0.96	0.08
		Min.	1.21	14.3	0.012	0.070	0.31	0.05
		Ave.	2.64	19.5	0.015	0.090	0.58	0.07
Tuna (oil	18	Max.	§	...	0.082	0.170	15.50	0.56
removed)		Min.	§	...	0.016	0.090	7.60	0.13
		Ave.	§	...	0.048	0.120	12.40	0.34

† In some instances all samples of a given product were not analyzed for all vitamin factors.

‡ Determined as calcium pantothenate. The relationship of pantothenic acid to human nutrition has not been established.

§ See Table V for vitamin A values of fish products.

TABLE IV

Biotin, Pyridoxine, "Folic Acid" Contents of
Selected Canned Foods *

Adapted from: Ives et al. (1946) and Neilands et al. (1947)†

Canned Foods	No. of Samples		Biotin	Pyridoxine	Content in micrograms per 100 grams	
					"Folic Acid" S. *Lactis* R. *Method*	"Folic Acid" L *Casei Method*
Asparagus	10	Max.	2.1	48	7.9	11.2
		Min.	1.0	17	3.2	6.2
		Ave.	1.7	30	5.8	9.0
Beans, green, cut	11	Max.	1.8	52	8.3	11.0
		Min.	1.1	18	1.2	4.0
		Ave.	1.3	32	2.9	7.7
Carrots	10	Max.	2.0	30	2.2	5.7
		Min.	1.0	14	1.0	2.2
		Ave.	1.5	22	1.3	4.1
Corn, yellow	10	Max.	2.7	100	2.4	6.9
		Min.	1.4	41	1.3	3.3
		Ave.	2.2	68	1.7	5.6
Grapefruit juice	11	Max.	0.4	27	0.7	1.6
		Min.	0.3	7	0.3	1.0
		Ave.	0.3	14	0.5	1.2
Mackerel *	9	Max.	23.0	290	. . .	1.2
		Min.	3.0	180	. . .	0.6
		Ave.	11.0	243	. . .	1.2
Peaches	9	Max.	0.3	20	1.2	2.9
		Min.	0.05	11	0.3	1.0
		Ave.	0.2	16	0.5	1.5
Peas	10	Max.	3.5	72	2.2	5.2
		Min.	1.4	24	1.0	3.2
		Ave.	2.1	46	1.7	4.4
Salmon *	21	Max.	19.0	500	4.4	10.2
		Min.	6.7	70	1.0	0.5
		Ave.	12.5	298	2.6	6.3
Sardines in brine *	6	Max.	34.0	300	. . .	. . .
		Min.	19.0	240	. . .	. . .
		Ave.	24.0	280	. . .	0.5 ‡

* Assays were conducted on combined solid-liquid portion of canned product except fish products, wherein only solid portion was analyzed. Products with "Folic Acid" determined by two methods are from Ives *et al.* (1946); other products from Neilands *et al.* (1947).

† For complete references, see Selected Bibliography, beginning page 245.

‡ One sample only assayed.

TABLE IV *(Concluded)*

Biotin, Pyridoxine, "Folic Acid" Contents of Selected Canned Foods *

Adapted from: Ives et al. (1946) and Neilands et al. (1947)†

Canned Foods	No. of Samples		Biotin	Pyridoxine	"Folic Acid" S. Lactis R. Method	"Folic Acid" L Casei Method
					Content in micrograms per 100 grams	
Sardines in oil *	8	Max.	6.0	200	. . .	2.7
		Min.	3.0	130	. . .	0.8
		Ave.	4.0	160	. . .	1.6
Sardines in tomato sauce *	5	Max.	33.0	250	. . .	. . .
		Min.	20.0	190	. . .	. . .
		Ave.	27.0	220	. . .	0.8 ‡
Spinach	10	Max.	3.1	80	16.5	51.3
		Min.	1.1	45	4.0	11.2
		Ave.	2.3	60	7.4	20.7
Tomatoes	10	Max.	2.4	98	4.1	8.2
		Min.	0.8	47	1.5	3.9
		Ave.	1.8	71	2.7	5.4
Tuna *	12	Max.	6.0	520	. . .	. . .
		Min.	3.0	370	. . .	. . .
		Ave.	3.0	440	. . .	0.6 ‡

* Assays were conducted on combined solid-liquid portion of canned product except fish products, wherein only solid portion was analyzed. Products with "Folic Acid" determined by two methods are from Ives *et al.* (1946) ; other products from Neilands *et al.* (1947).

† For complete references, see Selected Bibliography, beginning page 245.

‡ One sample only assayed.

TABLE V

Vitamin A and D Content of the Solid Portion of Selected Canned Fish

Adapted from: Neilands et al. (1947) and Pressley et al. (1944) *

		Vitamin A			Vitamin D	
Canned Fish	No. of Samples		U.S.P. Units per 100 grams †	No. of Samples		U.S.P. Units per 100 grams
Mackerel	17	Max.	913	9	Max.	250+
		Min.	27		Min.	165
		Ave.	155		Ave.	241
Salmon	16	Max.	340	11	Max.	500+
		Min.	50		Min.	500
		Ave.	145		Ave.	500
Sardines in brine	6	Max.	...	6	Max.	333
		Min.	...		Min.	333
		Ave.	< 27		Ave.	333
Sardines in oil	13	Max.	410	8	Max.	333
		Min.	70		Min.	250
		Ave.	226		Ave.	271
Sardines in tomato sauce	5	Max.	...	5	Max.	500
		Min.	...		Min.	333
		Ave.	< 27		Ave.	366
Shrimp, dry pack	3	Max.	77			
		Min.	47			
		Ave.	57			
Shrimp, wet pack	5	Max.	73			
		Min.	50			
		Ave.	60			
Tuna	18	Max.	33	12	Max.	333
		Min.	17		Min.	< 100
		Ave.	27		Ave.	234

* For complete references, see Selected Bibliography, beginning page 245.

† U.S.P. (United States Pharmacopoeia) units were calculated by multiplying reported milligrams of vitamin A per 100 grams by 3333.

TABLE VI

Proportion of Recommended Daily Allowances of Nutrients Supplied by Canned Food Servings *

Canned Foods	Weight gm.†	Protein Per Cent	Ca Per Cent	Fe Per Cent	Vitamin A Per Cent	Thiamine (Vitamin B_1) Per Cent	Riboflavin (Vitamin B_2) Per Cent	Niacin (Nicotinic Acid) Per Cent	Ascorbic Acid (Vitamin C) Per Cent
FRUITS:									
Apricots, syrup	122	1	1	7	52	2	1	3	6
Blackberries, syrup	113	1	2	24	4	1	1	2	9
Blueberries, syrup	113	1	1	48	1	1	1	1	20
Cherries, red, sour, pitted	113	1	1	26	20	2	1	1	9
Grapefruit sections	113	1	2	3	0	2	1	2	37
Peaches, cling, syrup	117	1	0	3	10	0	1	5	6
Peaches, freestone, syrup	117	1	1	3	8	0	1	4	4
Pears, syrup	117	0	1	5	0	1	1	1	2
Pineapple, sliced	122	1	2	7	1	6	1	1	8
Plums, purple (prunes) ‡	122	1	1	10	29	2	1	3	3
JUICES:									
Grapefruit juice	124	1	1	4	0	2	1	1	55
Grapefruit juice	186	1	2	6	0	3	2	2	82
Orange juice	124	1	1	5	4	6	1	2	58
Orange juice	186	2	2	8	6	9	2	3	87
Pineapple juice	121	1	2	3	1	4	1	1	14
Pineapple juice	186	1	3	5	2	6	2	2	21
Tomato juice	121	1	1	9	21	4	2	6	23
Tomato juice	182	2	1	14	31	6	3	9	35

* Recommended Dietary Allowances, Revised 1948, National Research Council, Number 129, October 1948, p. 16—based upon requirements for "physically active" man. Size servings are based on commonly served portions, representing equal divisions of the can content of each product as indicated in "Net Contents Statements for Canned Food Labels" 1949, National Canners Association.

† For terms of approximate measure, see Table X.

‡ Edible portion.

TABLE VI (Continued)

Proportion of Recommended Daily

Allowances of Nutrients Supplied by Canned Food Servings *

Canned Foods	Weight gm.†	Protein Per Cent	Ca Per Cent	Fe Per Cent	Vitamin A Per Cent	Thiamine (Vitamin B₁) Per Cent	Riboflavin (Vitamin B₂) Per Cent	Niacin (Nicotinic Acid) Per Cent	Ascorbic Acid (Vitamin C) Per Cent
VEGETABLES:									
Asparagus, green	108	3	2	15	11	5	6	6	22
Asparagus, white	108	2	2	8	1	4	3	5	22
Beans, baked	119	10	7	26	1	3	3	4	4
Beans, baked	179	14	10	39	2	4	4	6	7
Beans, green cut	108	2	4	11	6	2	2	2	5
Beans, Lima, green	113	7	3	23	3	2	2	4	11
Beets, cubed	113	2	2	17	0	1	1	1	5
Carrots, cubed	113	1	3	7	280	2	1	3	3
Corn, white, cream style	113	4	0	6	0.	2	3	8	8
Corn, yellow, cream style	113	3	0	6	3	2	3	7	8
Corn, white, whole grain	113	3	1	5	1	2	3	7	7
Corn, yellow, whole grain	113	3	0	4	3	2	3	6	7
Kraut	108	2	4	62	1	2	2	1	25
Mushrooms	90	4	1	4	0	1	10	10	2
Peas, Alaska	113	6	2	16	11	7	3	7	15
Peas, sweet	113	6	2	14	10	9	4	8	14
Peppers, sweet	38	0	0	6	25	1	2	2	60
Peppers, sweet	113	1	1	17	75	3	5	5	180
Pimientos	38	0	0	4	18	1	1	1	57
Pimientos	113	1	1	12	52	2	4	3	170
Spinach	102	3	9	18	112	1	6	2	18

* Recommended Dietary Allowances, Revised 1948, National Research Council, Number 129, October 1948, p. 16—based upon requirements for "physically active" man. Size servings are based on commonly served portions, representing equal divisions of the can content of each product as indicated in "Net Contents Statements for Canned Food Labels" 1949, National Canners Association.

† For terms of approximate measure, see Table X.

TABLE VI (*Concluded*)

Proportions of Recommended Daily
Allowances of Nutrients Supplied by Canned Food Servings *

	Weight gm. †	Protein Per Cent	Ca Per Cent	Fe Per Cent	Vitamin A Per Cent	Thiamine (Vitamin B_1) Per Cent	Riboflavin (Vitamin B_2) Per Cent	Niacin (Nicotinic Acid) Per Cent	Ascorbic Acid (Vitamin C) Per Cent
VEGETABLES (Continued):									
Sweetpotatoes	130	3	3	6	260	5	3	4	28
Tomatoes	108	2	1	5	21	4	2	5	24
Turnip greens	102	2	10	39	90	1	5	4	27
FISH:									
Mackerel	106	29	24	17	3	3	14	54	..
Salmon	113	35	21	6	2§	2	10	57	..
Sardines in oil **	60	17	21	18	3¶	1	5	19	..
Sardines in tomato sauce	106	27	40	36	1	1	14	35	..
Shrimp, dry pack	65	25	7	19	1	0	1	10	..
Shrimp, wet pack **	65	14	4	12	1	0	1	6	..
Tuna **	100	34	4	10	1	3	7	83	..

* Recommended Dietary Allowances, Revised 1948, National Research Council, Number 129, October 1948, p. 16—based upon requirements for "physically active" man. Size servings are based on commonly served portions, representing equal divisions of the can content of each product as indicated in "Net Contents Statements for Canned Food Labels" 1949, National Canners Association.
† For terms of approximate measure, see Table X.
§ Pink.
¶ Red.
** Drained.

TABLE VII

Proportion of Minimum Daily Requirements of Nutrients Supplied by Canned Food Servings *

Canned Foods	Weight gm.†	Vitamin A Per Cent	Thiamine (Vitamin B_1) Per Cent	Riboflavin (Vitamin B_2) Per Cent	Ascorbic Acid (Vitamin C) Per Cent	Calcium Per Cent‡ of M.D.R.	Phosphorus Per Cent‡ of M.D.R.	Iron Per Cent‡ of M.D.R.
FRUITS:								
Apricots, syrup	122	65	2	1	17	1	3	9
Blackberries, syrup	113	5	2	1	25	3	3	29
Blueberries, syrup	113	1	2	1	50	2	1	58
Cherries, red, sour, pitted	113	25	3	1	23	2	2	32
Grapefruit sections	113	0	4	1	95	2	2	3
Peaches, syrup, cling	117	13	1	1	17	2	2	4
Peaches, syrup, freestone	117	10	1	1	13	0	2	4
Pears, syrup	117	0	1	1	7	1	1	6
Pineapple, sliced	122	2	9	1	20	1	1	9
Plums, purple (prunes) ¶	122	37	3	1	7	3	2	12
JUICES:								
Grapefruit juice	124	1	4	1	135	1	2	5
Grapefruit juice	186	1	7	2	200	2	3	7
Orange juice	124	5	9	1	150	2	3	6
Orange juice	186	8	14	2	230	2	5	9
Pineapple juice	124	2	6	1	37	2	1	4
Pineapple juice	186	2	10	2	60	4	2	6
Tomato juice	121	26	7	2	60	1	3	11
Tomato juice	182	39	10	3	90	2	4	16

* Minimum Daily Requirements, Food and Drug Administration, Federal Register, November 22, 1941, p. 5921. Size servings are based on commonly served portions, representing equal divisions of the can content of each product as indicated in "Net Contents Statements for Canned Food Labels", 1949, National Canners Association.

† For terms of approximate measure, see Table X.

‡ For persons over 1 year of age, except pregnant or lactating women, for whom the percentages are half of these.

§ For persons over 6 years of age, except pregnant or lactating women, for whom the percentages are two-thirds of these.

¶ Edible portion.

TABLE VII (Continued)

Proportion of Minimum Daily Requirements of Nutrients Supplied by Canned Food Servings*

Canned Foods	Weight gm.†	Vitamin A Per Cent	Thiamine (Vitamin B₁) Per Cent	Riboflavin (Vitamin B₂) Per Cent	Ascorbic Acid (Vitamin C) Per Cent	Calcium Per Cent ‡ of M.D.R.	Phosphorus Per Cent ‡ of M.D.R.	Iron Per Cent § of M.D.R.
VEGETABLES:								
Asparagus, green	108	14	7	5	55	3	6	18
Asparagus, white	108	1	5	3	55	2	5	10
Beans, baked	119	2	4	3	10	9	17	31
Beans, baked	179	2	6	4	17	13	25	47
Beans, green cut	108	8	3	2	10	5	3	13
Beans, Lima, green	113	4	4	2	27	4	10	26
Beets, cubed	113	0	1	1	17	2	3	20
Carrots, cubed	113	350	3	1	7	4	3	8
Corn, white, cream style	113	0	4	3	23	0	8	7
Corn, yellow, cream style	113	4	3	3	23	0	9	7
Corn, white, whole grain	113	0	3	3	20	1	7	6
Corn, yellow, whole grain	113	4	3	3	20	1	8	5
Kraut	108	1	4	2	65	5	3	75
Mushrooms	90	0	1	9	7	1	8	5
Peas, Alaska	113	13	11	3	37	3	10	19
Peas, sweet	113	13	13	3	37	3	9	17
Peppers, sweet	38	31	2	2	150	0	1	7
Peppers, sweet	113	95	4	5	450	1	3	20
Pimientos	38	22	1	1	140	0	1	5
Pimientos	113	65	3	3	430	1	2	15
Spinach	102	140	2	5	43	12	4	21
Sweetpotatoes	130	320	7	3	70	4	9	8
Tomatoes	108	26	6	1	60	1	3	5
Turnip greens	102	110	2	5	65	14	4	47

See footnotes on page 231.

TABLE VII (*Concluded*)

Proportion of Minimum Daily Requirements of Nutrients Supplied by Canned Food Servings *

Canned Foods	Weight gm.†	Vitamin A Per Cent	Thiamine (Vitamin B₁) Per Cent	Riboflavin (Vitamin B₂) Per Cent	Ascorbic Acid (Vitamin C) Per Cent	Calcium Per Cent ‡ of M.D.R.	Phosphorus Per Cent ‡ of M.D.R.	Iron Per Cent § of M.D.R.
FISH:								
Mackerel	106	3	4	11	...	32	39	20
Salmon	113	2** 9††	2	9	...	28	44	7
Sardines in oil ‡‡	60	4	1	4	...	28	35	21
Sardines in tomato sauce	106	...	1	13	...	54	24	44
Shrimp, dry pack	65	1	1	1	...	9	21	23
Shrimp, wet pack ‡‡	65	1	1	1	...	5	13	14
Tuna ‡‡	100	1	4	7	...	1	30	12

* Minimum Daily Requirements, Food and Drug Administration, Federal Register, November 22, 1941, p. 5921. Size servings are based on commonly served portions, representing equal divisions of the can content of each product as indicated in "Net Contents Statements for Canned Food Labels", 1949, National Canners Association.

† For terms of approximate measure, see Table X.

‡ For persons over 1 year of age, except pregnant or lactating women, for whom the percentages are half of these.

§ For persons over 6 years of age, except pregnant or lactating women, for whom the percentages are two-thirds of these.

¶ Edible portion.

** Pink.

†† Red.

‡‡ Drained.

TABLE VIII

Common Food Can Sizes

Can Name*	Dimensions† Diameter	Dimensions† Height	Canner's Designation‡	No. of Cans Per Case	Some Canned Foods for Which Ordinarily Used
2Z Mushroom ...	2-1/8"	2-1/4"	202 x 204	24, 48	Mushrooms
....	2-1/8"	2-7/8"	202 x 214	12, 24, 48	Infant foods
6Z	2-1/8"	3-1/2"	202 x 308	24, 48, 100	Tomato paste, tomato sauce
....	2-1/2"	1-9/16"	208 x 109	24, 48, 96	Meat spreads
5Z	2-11/16"	2"	211 x 200	24, 48, 96	Olives, lemon and lime juice
Small Cranberry	2-11/16"	2-3/8"	211 x 206	24, 48	Cranberry sauce
4Z Mushroom ...	2-11/16"	2-3/4"	211 x 212	12, 24	Mushrooms
....	2-11/16"	2-7/8"	211 x 214	12, 24	Infant foods
8Z Short	2-11/16"	3"	211 x 300	24, 36, 48, 72, 96	Tomato sauce, specialties
8Z Tall	2-11/16"	3-1/4"	211 x 304	24, 36, 48, 72	Some vegetables & fruits, meat products, fish products, specialties
No. 1 Picnic ..	2-11/16"	4"	211 x 400	24, 48	Vegetables, some fruit juices, soups, meat products, fish products, specialties
No. 211 Cylinder	2-11/16"	4-7/8"	211 x 414	24, 36, 48	Fruit juices, tomato juice
Pint Olive	2-11/16"	6"	211 x 600	12, 24	Olives
4Z Pimientos ...	3"	1-1/2"	300 x 108	48, 96	Pimientos
7Z Pimientos ...	3"	2-3/8"	300 x 206	24, 48, 96	Pimientos
8Z Mushroom ...	3"	4"	300 x 400	12, 24, 48	Mushrooms
No. 300	3"	4-7/16"	300 x 407	24, 36, 48	Vegetables, some fruits, juices, soups, meat products, fish products, specialties
	3"	4-9/16"	300 x 409	24, 48	Meat products
	3"	4-11/16"	300 x 411	24, 48	Pimientos

* Names used by the Committee on Simplification of Container Sizes.
† Nominal over-all dimensions; actual dimensions will vary within manufacturing tolerances and with type of construction used.
‡ The can size designation used in the industry is derived from the nominal dimensions. The first digit represents inches, the next two the extra fraction expressed as sixteenths of an inch. The diameter is cited first, followed by the height. Example: 307 x 512 means 3-7/16" in diameter by 5-3/4" high.

TABLE VIII (Continued)

Common Food Can Sizes

Can Name *	Dimensions †		Canner's Designation ‡	No. of Cans Per Case	Some Canned Foods for Which Ordinarily Used
	Diameter	Height			
No. 300 Cylinder	3"	5-9/16"	300 x 509	24	Vegetable soup, pork and beans, specialties
No. 1 Pineapple	3-1/16"	4"	301 x 400	48	Pineapple
No. 1 Tall	3-1/16"	4-11/16"	301 x 411	24, 48	Fruits, some vegetables, juices, fish products, specialties
No. 303	3-3/16"	4-3/8"	303 x 406	12, 24, 36	Vegetables, some fruits and juices, soups, specialties
No. 303 Cylinder	3-3/16"	5-9/16"	303 x 509	12, 24	Tomato juice, fruit juice, soups, specialties
No. 1 Flat	3-7/16"	2-3/16"	307 x 203	48	Pineapple
Kitchenette	3-7/16"	2-7/8"	307 x 214	24, 36	Pork and beans
No. 2 Vacuum	3-7/16"	3-3/8"	307 x 306	24	Vacuum packed vegetables
No. 95	3-7/16"	4"	307 x 400	24	Some conventional and vacuum packed vegetables
No. 2	3-7/16"	4-9/16"	307 x 409	12, 24	Most commonly used size fruits, vegetables, juices, soups, specialties
No. 2XT	3-7/16"	5-3/8"	307 x 506	24	Pineapple
Jumbo	3-7/16"	5-5/8"	307 x 510	12, 24	Pork & beans, mushrooms
No. 2 Cylinder	3-7/16"	5-3/4"	307 x 512	24	Tomato juice, fruit juice, some soups, specialties
No. 2 Tall	3-7/16"	6-1/4"	307 x 604	12, 24	Asparagus
Quart Olive	3-7/16"	7-1/4"	307 x 704	12, 24	Olives
No. 1-1/4	4-1/16"	2-15/32"	401 x 207.5	36, 48	Pineapple
No. 2-1/2	4-1/16"	4-11/16"	401 x 411	12, 24	Fruits, some vegetables, some juices, meat products

* Names used by the Committee on Simplification of Container Sizes.

† Nominal over-all dimensions; actual dimensions will vary within manufacturing tolerances and with type of construction used.

‡ The can size designation used in the industry is derived from the nominal dimensions. The first digit represents inches, the next two the extra fraction expressed as sixteenths of an inch. The diameter is cited first, followed by the height. Example: 307 x 512 means 3-7/16" in diameter by 5-3/4" high.

TABLE VIII (*Concluded*)
Common Food Can Sizes

Can Name *	Dimensions † Diameter	Dimensions † Height	Canner's Designation ‡	No. of Cans Per Case	Same Canned Foods for Which Ordinarily Used
No. 3 Vacuum ...	4-1/4"	3-7/16"	404 x 307	24	Some vegetables, meat products
No. 3 Cylinder...	4-1/4"	7"	404 x 700	12	Fruit juices, tomato juice
No. 5	5-1/8"	5-5/8"	502 x 510	12	Fruits, juices, some vegetables, specialties
No. 10	6-3/16"	7"	603 x 700	6	Vegetables, fruits, juices, some meat and fish products, soups, specialties
No. 1 Square...	3" wide 3½" long	3-1/2"	300x308x308	24, 48	Asparagus
No. 2½ Square.	3" wide 3½" long	6-1/4"	300x308x604	24	Asparagus
12Z Oblong	2-1/8" wide 3-7/8" long	3-3/16"	314x202x303	24	Meat products

* Names used by the Committee on Simplification of Container Sizes.
† Nominal over-all dimensions; actual dimensions will vary within manufacturing tolerances and with type of construction used.
‡ The can size designation used in the industry is derived from the nominal dimensions. The first digit represents inches, the next two the extra fraction expressed as sixteenths of an inch. The diameter is cited first, followed by the height. Example: 307 x 512 means 3-7/16" in diameter by 5-3/4" high.

TABLE IX

Servings per Unit for Various Canned Foods in Common Can Sizes

| Canned Foods | Container Size | Net Weight or Volume | Approximate | | Size of Each Serving |
			Cups or Pieces	Servings per Container	
FRUITS:					
Apples; Applesauce; Berries; Cherries; Grapes; Grapefruit and Orange Sections; Fruit Cocktail; Fruits for Salad; Sliced Peaches; Pears; Pineapple Chunks, Crushed, Tidbits	8 Z Tall	8½–8⅜ oz.	1 cup	2	½ cup
	No. 2	1 lb. 4 oz.	2¼–2½ cups	5	½ cup
	No. 2½	1 lb. 13 oz.	3¼–3½ cups	7	½ cup
	No. 10	6 lb. 2 oz. to 6 lb. 12 oz.	12–13 cups	25	½ cup
Apricots, Whole (Medium Size)	No. 2	1 lb. 4 oz.	10–13	5	2–3 apricots
	No. 2½	1 lb. 13 oz.	15–18	7	2–3 apricots
	No. 10	6 lb. 10 oz	50–64	25	2–3 apricots
Apricots, Halves (Medium Size)	No. 2	1 lb. 4 oz.	18–24	5	3–4 halves
	No. 2½	1 lb. 13 oz.	26–35	7	3–4 halves
	No. 10	6 lb. 10 oz.	93–129	25	3–4 halves
Peaches, Halves (Medium Size)	No. 2	1 lb. 4 oz.	9–12	5	2 halves
	No. 2½	1 lb. 13 oz.	13–18	7	2 halves
Pears, Halves (Medium Size)	No. 10	6 lb. 10 oz.	45–66	25	2 halves

Note: The net weight of various foods in the same size can will vary with the density of the food. For the most part only minimum weights are shown in the table.

Cups or pieces and servings in the table have been given in approximates; and sizes of servings are given in rounded numbers in order to furnish a practical guide.

TABLE IX (Continued)

Servings per Unit for Various Canned Foods in Common Can Sizes

Canned Foods	Container Size	Net Weight or Volume	Approximate Cups or Pieces	Servings per Container	Size of Each Serving
Pineapple, Sliced	No. 1 Flat	9 oz.	4	2	2 slices
	No. 2	1 lb. 4 oz.	10	5	2 slices
	No. 2½	1 lb. 14 oz.	8	8	1 slice
	No. 10	6 lb. 12 oz.	28-50	25	1 large or 2 small slices
Plums; Prunes	No. 2	1 lb. 4 oz.	9-11	5	2-3 plums
	No. 2½	1 lb. 14 oz.	12-16	7	2-3 plums
	No. 10	6 lb. 10 oz.	41-59	25	2-3 plums
Figs	No. 2	1 lb. 4 oz.	13-17	5	3 figs
	No. 2½	1 lb. 14 oz.	18-24	7	3 figs
	No. 10	7 lb.	67-89	25	3 figs
Cranberry Sauce	No. 300	1 lb.	2 cups	8	¼ cup
	No. 10	7 lb. 5 oz.	12-13 cups	50	¼ cup
Olives, Ripe *	8 Z Tall	4½ oz.	....	.....	3 olives
	No. 1 Tall	9 oz.	....	.....	3 olives
	No. 2½	1 lb. 2 oz.	....	.....	3 olives
	No. 10	4 lb. 2 oz.	....	.....	3 olives
JUICES: Apple; Cherry; Cranberry; Grape; Grapefruit; Grapefruit-Orange; Lo- ganberry; Nectar; Orange; Pineapple; Prune; Tangerine; Car- rot; Kraut; Tomato; Vegetable; Vegetable Cocktail	No. 211	12 oz.	1½ cups	3	4 oz.
	Cylinder	....	....	2	6 oz.
	No. 2	1 pt. 2 oz.	2¼-2½ cups	5	4 oz.
		....	....	3	6 oz.
	No. 303	1 pt. 3 oz.	2¾ cups	6	4 oz.
	Cylinder	....	....	4	6 oz.
	No. 2 Cylinder	1 pt. 7 oz.	3 cups	6	4 oz.
		....	....	4	6 oz.
	No. 3 Cylinder	1 qt. 14 oz.	5¾ cups	12	4 oz.
		....	....	8	6 oz.

TABLE IX (Continued)
Servings per Unit for Various Canned Foods in Common Can Sizes

Canned Foods	Container Size	Net Weight or Volume	Approximate		
			Cups or Pieces	Servings per Container	Size of Each Serving
Lemon; Lime	No. 10	3 qt.	12 cups	24	4 oz.
	5 Z	....	....	16	6 oz.
		5 oz.	⅔ cup	....	....
VEGETABLES:					
Asparagus Cuts; Beans, Green and Wax, Kidney; Lima; Beets; Carrots; Corn; Hominy; Okra; Vacuum	8 Z Tall	8½ oz.	1 cup	2	½ cup
	No. 1 Picnic	10½ oz.	1⅓ cups	3	⅓-½ cup
	No. 2	12 oz.	1½-1¾ cups	4	⅓-½ cup
Onions; Peas; Peas and Carrots; Black Eye Peas; Pimientos†; Peppers†; Red, Sweet; Pumpkin; Sauerkraut; Spinach and other Greens; Squash; Succotash; Sweetpotatoes; Tomatoes; Mixed Vegetables; Potatoes, White, Cut, Sliced	No. 303	1 lb.	2 cups	4	½ cup
	No. 2	1 lb. 4 oz.	2¼-2½ cups	5	½ cup
	No. 2½	1 lb. 13 oz.	3¼-3½ cups	7	½ cup
	No. 10	6 lb. 2 oz. to 6 lb. 12 oz.	12-13 cups	25	½ cup
Asparagus Spears (Medium Size)	No. 1 Square	1 lb.	18-24 spears	4	6 spears
	No. 2	1 lb. 3 oz.	20-30 spears	5	6 spears
	No. 2½	1 lb. 12 oz.	35-44 spears	7	6 spears
	No. 10	6 lb. 7 oz.	150 spears	25	6 spears
Potatoes, White, Whole	No. 2	1 lb. 4 oz.	10-15	5	2-3 potatoes

Note: The net weight of various foods in the same size can will vary with the density of the food. For the most part only minimum weights are shown in the table.

Cups or pieces and servings in the table have been given in approximates; and sizes of servings are given in rounded numbers in order to furnish a practical guide. The number of olives per container varies as to size of the olives.

* Declared as drained weight. The weight of olives per container varies as to size of the olives.
† Pimientos and Sweet Red Peppers also come in smaller can sizes.

TABLE IX *(Continued)*

Servings per Unit for Various Canned Foods in Common Can Sizes

Canned Foods	Container Size	Approximate: Net Weight or Volume	Approximate: Cups or Pieces	Approximate: Servings per Container	Approximate: Size of Each Serving
VEGETABLES (Continued):					
Beans, Baked; with Pork; in Sauce	No. 300	15½ oz.	2 cups	3-4	½-¾ cup
	Jumbo	1 lb. 10 oz.	3 cups	4-6	½-¾ cup
	No. 10	6 lb. 14 oz.	12-13 cups	16-25	½-¾ cup
Mushrooms	2 Z	3¼ oz.	⅓ cup	1	⅓ cup
	4 Z	6¾ oz.	⅔ cup	2	⅓ cup
	8 Z	12½ oz.	1½ cups	4	⅓ cup
	No. 10	6 lb. 7 oz.	12 cups	36	⅓ cup
INFANT FOODS:					
Vegetables and Fruits:					
Infant (Strained, Homogenized)	....	4½ oz.	9 tbsp.	....	....
Junior (Chopped)	....	4½ oz.	9 tbsp.	....	....
	....	7½ oz.	14 tbsp.	....	....
Meats:					
Infant (Strained)	....	3½ oz.	6 tbsp.	....	....
Junior (Chopped)	....	3½ oz.	6 tbsp.	....	....
Soups:					
Infant and Junior	....	4½ oz.	9 tbsp.	....	....
SOUPS:	No. 1 Picnic	10½-12 oz.	1¼-1½ cups	2 §	¾ cup
	No. 303	1 lb.	2 cups	3	¾ cup
	No. 300 Cylinder	1 lb. 2 oz.	2¼ cups	3-4	¾ cup
	No. 303 Cylinder	1 lb. 5 oz.	2½ cups	4	¾ cup
	No. 3 Cylinder	3 lb. 2 oz.	6¼ cups	8-9	¾ cup
	No. 10	6 lb. 8 oz.	12-13 cups	16	¾ cup

TABLE IX (Continued)
Servings per Unit for Various Canned Foods in Common Can Sizes

Canned Foods	Container Size	Net Weight or Volume	Approximate		Servings per Container	Size of Each Serving
			Cups or Pieces			
MEATS:						
Chili Con Carne	No. 300	15½-16 oz.	2 cups		3-4	½-⅔ cup
	No. 10	6 lb. 12 oz.	12 cups		20	½-⅔ cup
Corned Beef	No. 1	12 oz.	....		4	3 oz.
	No. 6	6 lb.	....		30	3 oz.
Corned Beef Hash	1 lb.	1 lb.	2 cups		3-4	½-⅔ cup
	No. 10	5 lb. 8 oz. to 5 lb. 14 oz.	12 cups		18-24	½-⅔ cup
Deviled Ham	No. ¼	3 oz.	⅓ cup		3-4	1½ table-spoons
Deviled Meat; Potted Meat; Meat Spreads	No. ¼	2-3¼ oz.	⅓ cup		3-4	1½ table-spoons
	No. ½	5½ oz.	¾ cup		8	1½ table-spoons
Luncheon Meat; Pork Loaf	12 Z Oblong	12 oz.	....		4	2 slices (3½" x 1¾" x ⅜")
	6 lb.	6 lb.	....		32	2 slices
Veal Loaf	7 oz.	7 oz.	....		2-3	2 slices (3½" x 1¾" x ⅜")
Tongues, Lunch	No. ½	6 oz.	....		2	3 oz.
	No. 1	12 oz.	....		4	3 oz.
Tongue, Ox	....	1-2 lb.	....		4-8	4 oz.

Note: The net weight of various foods in the same size can will vary with the density of the food. For the most part only minimum weights are shown in the table.

Cups or pieces and servings in the table have been given in approximates; and sizes of servings are given in rounded numbers in order to furnish a practical guide.

§ Servings for condensed soups should be based on quantity after liquid has been added. The number of servings would be twice those stated here.

TABLE IX ***(Concluded)***

Servings per Unit for Various Canned Foods in Common Can Sizes

Canned Foods	Container Size	Approximate Net Weight or Volume	Approximate Cups or Pieces	Approximate Servings per Container	Approximate Serving
MEATS: (Contd.)					
Hams, Whole (Small)	....	9-11 lbs.	....	20-35	2 slices
(Medium to Large)	....	11-13 lbs.	....	35-45	(4″ x 3″ x ⅛″)
Poultry, Chicken; Turkey;	....	4½ oz.	....	1-2	3 oz.
(Boned)	....	6 oz.	....	2	3 oz.
	....	11 oz.	....	4	3 oz.
	....	2 lb. 3 oz.	....	12	3 oz.
Sausage, Pork; Frankfurters	8 Z	8 oz.	11-12	3-4	3 sausages
	....	12 oz.	8-9 large	4	2 sausages
Vienna Sausage	No. ½	4 oz.	8-10	2	4-5 sausages
	....	9 oz.	16-20	4	4-5 sausages
FISH AND SHELLFISH:					
Clams	No. 1 Picnic	10½ oz.	1¼ cups	3	½ cup
	No. 300	15 oz.	2 cups	4	½ cup
Crabmeat	Squat	6½ oz.	¾ cup	2	⅓-½ cup
Mackerel	1 lb. Tall	1 lb.	2 cups	4	½ cup
Salmon	½ lb. Flat	7¾ oz.	1 cup	2	½ cup
	1 lb. Flat	15½ oz.	2 cups	4	½ cup
	1 lb. Tall	1 lb.	2 cups	4	½ cup
Sardines	No. ¼	3¼ oz.	6-10	1½	5-7 sardines
Sardines (Pilchards)	No. 1 Oval	15 oz.	6-7 large	4	1½ sardines
Shrimp* (Medium Size)	8 Z Short	5 oz.	24-30	3	10 shrimp
	No. 1 Picnic	7 oz.	31-38	3-4	10 shrimp
Tuna	No. ½	7 oz.	1 cup	2	½ cup
	No. 1	13 oz.	1¾ cups	4	½ cup

Note: The net weight of various foods in the same size can will vary with the density of the food. For the most part only minimum weights are shown in the table.

Cups or pieces and servings in the table have been given in approximates; and sizes of servings are given in rounded numbers in order to furnish a practical guide.

* Declared as drained weight.

TABLE X

Nutritive Values of Canned Food Servings

Canned Foods	Size of Serving Weight gm.	Size of Serving Approximate Measure	Calories	Protein gm.	Fat gm.	CHO gm.	Ca mg.	P mg.	Fe mg.	Vitamin A I.U.	Thiamine (Vit. B$_1$) mg.	Riboflavin (Vit. B$_2$) mg.	Niacin (Nicotinic Acid) mg.	Ascorbic Acid (Vit. C) mg.
FRUITS:														
Apricots, syrup	122	4 med. size halves & 2 T syrup	105	.6	.2	25.0	9.8	19.5	.85	2,650	.022	.024	.42	5
Blackberries, syrup	113	½ cup	95	.8	.2	22.4	20.3	21.5	2.94	200	.015	.021	.24	7
Blueberries, syrup	113	½ cup	51	.7	.2	11.5	12.4	6.8	5.76	38	.016	.016	.21	15
Cherries, red, sour, pitted	113	½ cup	60	.9	.3	13.3	12.4	13.6	3.16	980	.031	.018	.21	7
Grapefruit, segments	113	½ cup	87	.7	.1	20.9	14.7	15.8	.34	18	.040	.024	.24	28
Peaches, cling	117	2 med. size halves & 2 T syrup	95	.6	.1	22.7	3.5	12.9	.35	530	.008	.023	.70	5
Peaches, freestone	117	2 med. size halves & 2 T syrup	101	.6	.1	24.3	4.7	14.0	.35	390	.009	.023	.64	4
Pears, syrup	117	2 med. size halves & 2 T syrup	88	.4	.1	21.2	7.0	8.2	.59	12	.011	.021	.23	2
Pineapple, sliced	122	2 small or 1 large slice & 2 T syrup	124	.5	.2	30.1	24.4	9.8	.85	60	.085	.026	.21	6
Plums, purple (prunes)*	122	3 plums & 2 T syrup	113	.6	.1	27.6	9.8	15.9	1.22	1,475	.028	.024	.44	2
JUICES:														
Grapefruit juice	124	4 fl. ozs.	55	.6	.1	12.8	9.9	16.1	.50	21	.043	.024	.21	41
Grapefruit juice	186	6 fl. ozs.	82	.9	.2	19.2	14.9	24.2	.74	31	.065	.035	.32	61
Orange juice	124	4 fl. ozs.	61	1.0	.2	13.5	12.4	23.6	.62	200	.092	.025	.30	46
Orange juice	186	6 fl. ozs.	91	1.5	.4	20.3	18.6	35.3	.93	310	.138	.037	.45	69
Pineapple juice	124	4 fl. ozs.	73	.5	.1	17.6	18.6	11.2	.37	60	.064	.022	.22	11
Pineapple juice	186	6 fl. ozs.	110	.7	.2	26.4	27.9	16.7	.56	95	.097	.033	.33	17
Tomato juice	121	4 fl. ozs.	25	1.0	.1	5.0	8.5	21.8	1.09	1,050	.067	.034	.93	17
Tomato juice	182	6 fl. ozs.	38	1.5	.2	7.5	12.7	32.8	1.64	1,575	.100	.051	1.40	27
VEGETABLES:														
Asparagus, white	108	6 med. size spears	22	1.7	.3	2.9	16.2	35.6	.97	55	.054	.063	.76	16
Asparagus, green	108	6 med. size spears	22	2.1	.3	2.7	19.4	46.4	1.84	550	.072	.099	.89	16
Beans, baked	119	½ cup	142	6.7	2.4	22.6	66.6	126.1	3.09	60	.040	.050	.61	3
Beans, baked	179	¾ cup	213	10.1	3.6	34.0	100.2	189.7	4.65	90	.061	.075	.91	5
Beans, green, cut	108	½ cup	21	1.2	.1	3.8	36.7	22.7	1.30	320	.030	.039	.35	3

* Edible portion.

TABLE X (*Concluded*)
Nutritive Values of Canned Food Servings

Canned Foods	Size of Serving Weight gm.	Approximate Measure	Calories	Protein gm.	Fat gm.	CHO gm.	Ca mg.	P mg.	Fe mg.	Vitamin A I.U.	Thiamine (Vit. B₁) mg.	Riboflavin (Vit. B₂) mg.	Niacin (Nicotinic Acid) mg.	Ascorbic Acid (Vit. C) mg.
Vegetables (Contd.)														
Beans, Lima, green	113	½ cup	77	4.6	.3	13.9	29.4	75.7	2.71	170	.037	.045	.60	8
Beets, cubed	113	½ cup	38	1.0	.1	8.4	15.8	19.2	2.03	17	.009	.026	.17	5
Carrots, cubed	113	½ cup	32	.8	.2	6.6	28.3	22.6	.79	13,900	.025	.023	.40	2
Corn, white, cream style	113	½ cup	103	2.5	.7	21.6	2.3	62.2	.68	18	.035	.055	1.22	7
Corn, yellow, cream style	113	½ cup	104	2.4	.7	22.0	3.4	64.4	.68	150	.034	.059	1.06	7
Corn, white, whole grain	113	½ cup	79	2.2	.7	16.2	5.7	50.9	.57	18	.025	.051	1.02	6
Corn, yellow, whole grain	113	½ cup	85	2.2	.7	17.6	4.5	56.5	.45	170	.028	.051	.95	6
Kraut	108	⅔ cup	23	1.1	.2	4.1	38.9	19.4	7.45	55	.037	.044	.12	19
Mushrooms	90	⅓ cup	17	2.6	.1	1.4	5.4	61.2	.45	15	.014	.171	1.44	2
Peas, Alaska	113	½ cup	69	4.0	.3	12.5	22.6	74.6	1.92	530	.108	.060	.97	11
Peas, sweet	113	½ cup	60	3.8	.5	10.2	21.5	65.5	1.70	510	.127	.064	1.13	11
Peppers, sweet	38	1 med. size	12	.3	.2	2.3	3.0	7.2	.68	1,250	.015	.030	.27	45
Peppers, sweet	113	3 med. size	35	.9	.5	6.8	9.0	21.5	2.03	3,750	.044	.090	.79	134
Pimientos	38	1 med. size	9	.3	.2	1.6	2.3	5.7	.49	870	.010	.023	.15	43
Pimientos	113	3 med. size	27	1.0	.5	4.9	6.8	17.0	1.47	2,600	.028	.068	.45	128
Spinach	102	½ cup	21	2.0	.4	2.4	86.7	26.5	2.14	5,600	.018	.102	.33	13
Sweetpotatoes	130	½ cup	143	2.0	.1	33.4	27.3	65.0	.78	12,900	.069	.056	.64	21
Tomatoes	108	½ cup	24	1.1	.3	4.3	6.5	20.5	.54	1,050	.059	.029	.75	18
Turnip greens	102	½ cup	19	1.5	.3	2.6	102.0	30.6	4.69	4,475	.015	.092	.59	20
FISH:														
Mackerel	106	½ cup	209	20.4	14.0	.4	238.5	290.4	2.01	110	.036	.212	8.29	..
Salmon	113	½ cup	168	24.2	7.9	.1	207.9	330.0	.68	75† / 340‡	.024	.181	8.83	..
Sardines in oil §	60	5 med. or 7 small	165	11.8	13.0	.3	212.4	260.4	2.10	140	.014	.078	3.00	..
Sardines in tomato sauce	106	1½ large	223	18.9	15.7	1.6	403.9	178.1	4.35		.011	.265	5.30	..
Shrimp, dry pack	65	10-12 med. size	78	17.4	.9	.3	67.6	156.0	2.28	43	.006	.021	1.45	..
Shrimp, wet pack §	65	10-12 med. size	44	9.8	.5	.3	35.8	96.9	1.43	40	.005	.020	.88	..
Tuna §	100	½ cup	255	24.0	17.3	.9	8.0	224.0	1.20	33	.037	.140	10.20	..

† Pink.
‡ Red.
§ Drained.

TABLE XI

Per Cent of Recommended Daily Intake* of Essential Amino Acids Furnished by Average Size Servings of Various Canned Fish and Meat Products †

Adapted from: Dunn et al. (1949) and Neilands et al. (1949)

	Size of Serving gm.	Isoleucine	Leucine	Lysine	Methionine	Phenylalanine	Threonine	Tryptophan	Valine
FISH PRODUCTS:									
Fish Flakes	100	95	88	131	33	41	117	48	80
Mackerel	106	75	73	111	28	35	100	44	70
Salmon	113	76	73	109	30	36	96	39	76
Sardines in Oil	60	44	42	63	16	21	57	19	41
Sardines in Tomato Sauce	106	64	65	101	26	33	85	39	64
Shrimp‡	65	57	66	79	23	30	63	30	48
Tuna	100	89	85	132	32	43	110	47	84
MEAT PRODUCTS:									
Roast Beef	113	86	86	131	30	40	109	44	77
Spiced Ham	113	54	57	82	18	28	65	30	50
Whole Ham	113	64	65	101	21	31	76	35	61

* Recommended daily dietary intake suggested by W. C. Rose, Fed. Proc., 8, 546 (1949) are: Isoleucine 1.4 gm., Leucine, 2.2 gm., Lysine 1.6 gm., Methionine, 2.2 gm., Phenylalanine 2.2 gm., Threonine 1.0 gm., Tryptophan 0.5 gm., and Valine 1.6 gm.
† For complete reference, see Selected Bibliography, beginning page 245.
‡ Only solid portion was analyzed because the liquid is customarily discarded.

SELECTED BIBLIOGRAPHY OF THE NUTRITIVE VALUE OF CANNED FOODS

Research Papers

Alexander, O. R. and Feaster, J. F. *Thiamin and Ascorbic Acid Values of Raw and Canned Peas*. Food Research 12, 468-473, 1947.

Alexander, O. R., Sallee, E. D. and Taylor, L. V. *Variations in Chemical Composition of Raw and Canned Peas*. Food Research 8, 254-264, 1943.

Arnold, A. and Elvehjem, C. A. *Processing and Thiamin*. Food Research 4, 547-553, 1938.

Beattie, H. G., Wheeler, K. A. and Pederson, C. S. *Changes Occurring in Fruit Juices During Storage*. Food Research 8, 395-404, 1943.

Bailey, B. E. *The Value of the Bones of Canned Salmon in the Prevention and Cure of Rickets*. Fisheries Res. Board Can. Progress Repts. Pacific Stations, 41, 17-19, 1939.

Bailey, E. M. *Ascorbic Acid Content of Canned Citrus Juices*. Conn. Agr. Expt. Sta. Bull. No. 437, 458, 1940.

Bedford, C. L. and McGregor, M. A. *Effect of Canning on the Ascorbic Acid and Thiamine in Vegetables*. J. Am. Dietet. Assoc. 24, 866-869, 1948.

Bessey, O. A. *Report on the Determination of Ascorbic Acid (Vitamin C) in Citrus Fruits and Tomatoes*. J. Assoc. Off. Agr. Chem. 27, 537-540, 1944.

Beuk, J. F., Charnock, F. W. and Rice, E. E. *The Effect of Heat on the Availability of Pork Protein in Vivo and in Vitro*. J. Biol. Chem. 180, 1243-1251, 1949.

Blatt, M. L., Jacobs, H. M., Murphy, J. B. and Zeldes, M. *The Addition of Homogenized Vegetables to the Diet of the Young Infant*. Arch. Pediat. 58, 40, 1941.

Boyd, J. M. and Peterson, G. T. *Quality of Canned Orange Juice*. Ind. Eng. Chem. 37, 370-373, 1945.

Brenion, H. D. and Cameron, C. R. *Retention of Ascorbic Acid in Canned Fruit Juices and Tomatoes During Storage After Opening*. Can. J. Pub. Health 38, No. 6, 283-285, 1947.

Brenner, S., Wodicka, V. O. and Dunlop, S. G. *Effect of High Temperature Storage on the Retention of Nutrients in Canned Foods*. Food Technology 2, 207-221, 1948.

Brush, M. K., Hinman, W. F. and Halliday, E. G. *The Nutritive Value of Canned Foods. V. Distribution of Water Soluble Vitamins Between Solid and Liquid Portions of Canned Vegetables and Fruits*. J. Nutrition 28, 131-140, 1944.

Bryan, A. H., Turner, D., Lotwin, G. and Huenemann, R. L. *The Estimation of the Ascorbic Acid Content of the Diet.* J. Am. Dietet. Assoc. **16**, 891-897, 1940.

Cailleau, R., Kidder, L. E. and Morgan, A. F. *The Thiamine Content of Raw and Parboiled Rices.* Cereal Chem. **22**, 50-60, 1945.

Clifcorn, L. E. *The Nutritive Value of Canned Foods. I. Introduction and Sampling Procedure.* J. Nutrition **28**, 101-105, 1944.

Clifcorn, L. E. and Heberlein, D. G. *Thiamine Content of Vegetables, Effect of Commercial Canning.* Ind. Eng. Chem. **36**, 168-171, 1944.

Clifcorn, L. E. and Peterson, G. T. *The Retention of Vitamin C in Tomato Juice.* Supplement to N.C.A. Information Letter No. 1200, 81-85, 1947.

Cohee, R. F., Jr., and Goodale, R. *Vitamin C Losses During Storage of Tomato Juice.* Food Packer **26**, No. 10, 43-44, 60, 1945.

Cosner, L. B. and Schuck, C. *Suitability of the Bourquin-Sherman Diet for Riboflavin Assays and Results Obtained in the Assay of Evaporated Milk.* J. Nutrition **35**, 725-732, 1948.

Council on Foods. *The Vitamin C Content of Commercially Canned Tomato Juice and Other Fruit Juices as Determined by Chemical Tritation.* J. Am. Med. Assoc. **110**, 650-651, 1938.

Daniels, A. L. *Comparison of Vitamin B_1 Content of Raw and Evaporated Milk by the 10-Day Bioassay Method.* Proc. Soc. Exptl. Biol. and Med. **38**, 212-216, 1938.

Daniels, A. L. *Further Evidence of Destruction of Thiamine in Evaporated Milk.* Am. J. Diseases Children **62**, 127-129, 1941.

Davidson, L. T., Merritt, K. K. and Chipman, S. S. *Prophylaxis of Rickets in Infants with Irradiated Evaporated Milk.* Am. J. Diseases Children **53**, 1-21, 1937.

Daum, K., Aimone, M. and Hollister, S. *Ascorbic Acid in Institutional Food.* J. Am. Dietet. Assoc. **19**, 693-694, 1943.

DeFelice, D. and Fellers, C. R. *Carotene Content of Fresh, Frozen, Canned and Dehydrated Spinach.* Proc. Am. Soc. Hort. Sci. **35**, 728-733, 1938.

Doan, F. J. and Josephson, D. V. *Observations on the Ascorbic Acid Content of Evaporated Milk.* J. Dairy Sci. **26**, 1031-1041, 1943.

Doan, F. J. and Josephson, D. V. *Vacuum Sealing Will Retain Vitamin C in Evaporated Milk.* Food Industries **16**, 371-372, 416-417, 1944.

Dunker, C. F., Fellers, C. R. and Fitzgerald, G. A. *Stability of Vitamin C in Sweet Corn to Shipping, Freezing and Canning.* Food Research **2**, 41-50, 1937.

Dunker, C. F. and Fellers, C. R. *Vitamin C Content of Spinach.* Proc. Am. Soc. Hort. Sci. **36**, 500-504, 1939.

Dunn, M. S., Camien, M. N., Eiduson, S. and Malin, R. B. *XXXIII. The Nutritive Value of Canned Foods. I. Amino Acid Content of Fish and Meat Products.* J. Nutrition **39**, 177-185, 1949.

Esselen, W. B., Jr., and Woodward, R. A. *Effect of Containers and Other Factors on the Ascorbic Acid Content of Processed Tomato Juice*. Mass. Agr. Expt. Sta. Natl. Cooperative Project, Conservation of Nutritive Value of Foods, Progress Notes, 1945.

Feaster, J. F. and Alexander, O. R. *Planning Nutrition Studies Involving Canned Foods*. Ind. Eng. Chem. **36**, 172-176, 1944.

Feaster, J. F., Jackson, J. M., Greenwood, D. A. and Kraybill, H. R. *Vitamin Retention in Processed Meat—Effect of Storage*. Ind. Eng. Chem. **38**, 87-90, 1946.

Feaster, J. F., Mudra, A. E., Ives, M. and Tompkins, M. D. *Effect of Blanching Time on Vitamin Retention in Canned Peas*. Canner **108**, No. 1, 27-30, 1949.

Feaster, J. F., Tompkins, M. D. and Ives, M. *Influence of Processing Technique on Vitamin Retention in Canned Corn*. Canner **104**, No. 11, 16, 18, 1947.

Feaster, J. F., Tompkins, M. D. and Ives, M. *Retentions of Vitamins in Low Acid Canned Foods*. Food Industries **20**, No. 1, 82-85, 218-222, 1948.

Fellers, C. R., Esselen, W. B. Jr. and Fitzgerald, G. A. *Vitamin B_1 and Vitamin B_2 (G) Content of Vegetables as Influenced by Quick-Freezing and Canning*. Food Research **5**, 495-502, 1940.

Fellers, C. R., Esselen, W. B. Jr., Maclinn, W. A. and Dunker, C. F. *Nutritive Studies on Fresh and Processed Fruits and Vegetables*. Mass. Agr. Expt. Sta. Bull. No. 355, 74, 1939.

Fellers, C. R. and Harris, S. G. *Canned Atlantic Crabmeat*. Ind. Eng. Chem. **32**, 592-594, 1940.

Fenton, F., Gleim, E., Albury, M., Visnyei, K. and McCartney, J. R. *Effect of Quantity Preparation Procedures on Vitamin Retention: Canned Peas*. J. Am. Dietet. Assoc. **21**, 700-702, 1945.

Filios, A. M. and Esselen, W. B. Jr. *The Vitamin Content of Canned and Cooked Fresh Mushrooms*. J. Am. Dietet. Assoc. **22**, 772-777, 1946.

Freed, M., Brenner, S. and Wodicka, V. O. *Prediction of Thiamin and Ascorbic Acid Stability in Stored Canned Foods*. Food Technology **3**, 148-151, 1949.

Gleim, E., Albury, M., Visnyei, K., McCartney, J. R. and Fenton, F. *Effect of Quantity Preparation Procedures on Vitamin Retention: Canned Tomatoes*. J. Am. Dietet. Assoc. **22**, 29-31, 1946.

Greenwood, D. A., Kraybill, H. R., Feaster, J. F. and Jackson, J. M. *Vitamin Retention in Processed Meat, Effect of Thermal Processing*. Ind. Eng. Chem. **36**, 922-927, 1944.

Guerrant, N. B. and Dutcher, R. A. *Further Observations Concerning the Relationship of Temperature of Blanching to Ascorbic Acid Retention in Green Beans*. Arch. Biochem. **18**, 353-359, 1948.

Guerrant, N. B., Fardig, O. B., Vavich, M. G. and Ellenberger, H. E. *Nutritive Value of Canned Foods. XXVII. Influence of Temperature and Time of Storage on Vitamin Content.* Ind. Eng. Chem. **40**, 2258-2263, 1948.

Guerrant, N. B., Vavich, M. G. and Dutcher, R. A. *Nutritive Value of Canned Foods. XIII. Influence of Temperature and Time of Storage on Vitamin Contents.* Ind. Eng. Chem. **37**, 1240-1243, 1945.

Guerrant, N. B., Vavich, M. G. and Fardig, O. B. *Nutritive Value of Canned Foods. XI. Comparison of Vitamin Values Obtained by Different Methods of Assay.* Ind. Eng. Chem., Anal. Ed. **17**, 710-713, 1945.

Guerrant, N. B., Vavich, M. G., Fardig, O. B., Dutcher, R. A. and Stern, R. M. *The Nutritive Value of Canned Foods. XX. Changes in the Vitamin Content of Foods During Canning.* J. Nutrition **32**, 435-458, 1946.

Guerrant, N. B., Vavich, M. G., Fardig, O. B., Ellenberger, H. A., Stern, R. M. and Coonen, N. H. *Nutritive Value of Canned Foods. XXIII. Effect of Duration and Temperature of Blanch on Vitamin Retention by Certain Vegetables.* Ind. Eng. Chem. **39**, 1000-1007, 1947.

Haagen-Smith, A. J., Strickland, A. G. R., Jeffreys, C. E. P. and Kirchner, J. G. *Studies on Vitamin Content of Canned Pineapple.* Food Research **11**, 142-147, 1946.

Hawley, E. E. *The Vitamin C Content of Fruit Juices.* J. Am. Dietet. Assoc. **13**, 261-262, 1937.

Hinman, W. F., Brush, M. K. and Halliday, E. G. *The Nutritive Value of Canned Foods. VI. Effect of Large-Scale Preparation for Serving on the Ascorbic Acid, Thiamine, and Riboflavin Content of Commercially-Canned Vegetables.* J. Am. Dietet. Assoc. **20**, 752-756, 1944.

Hinman, W. F., Brush, M. K. and Halliday, E. G. *The Nutritive Value of Canned Foods. VII. Effect of Small-Scale Preparation for Serving on the Ascorbic Acid, Thiamine, and Riboflavin Content of Commercially-Canned Vegetables.* J. Am. Dietet. Assoc. **21**, 7-10, 1945.

Hinman, W. F., Higgins, M. M. and Halliday, E. G. *The Nutritive Value of Canned Foods. XVIII. Further Studies on Carotene, Ascorbic Acid, and Thiamine.* J. Am. Dietet. Assoc. **23**, 226-231, 1947.

Hoar, W. S. and Barberie, M. *Distribution of Riboflavin in Fresh and Processed Fish.* Can. J. Research **23E**, 8, 1945.

Hodson, A. Z. *The Pyridoxine Content of Fresh, Pasteurized, Evaporated and Dried Milk.* J. Nutrition **27**, 415-418, 1944.

Hodson, A. Z. *The Nicotinic Acid, Pantothenic Acid, Choline and Biotin Content of Fresh, Irradiated Evaporated and Dry Milk.* J. Nutrition **29**, 137-142, 1945.

Hodson, A. Z. and Krueger, G. M. *Essential Amino Acid Content of Casein and Fresh and Processed Cow's Milk as Determined Microbiologically on Hydrolyzates.* Arch. Biochem. 10, 55-64, 1946.

Holmes, A. D., Piggott, M. G. and Tripp, F. *Comparative Costs of Vitamin C in Fresh and Commercially Canned Fruit and Vegetable Juices.* New Eng. J. Med. 225, 68-73, 1941.

Ives, M., Pollard, A. E., Elvehjem, C. A. and Strong, F. M. *Nutritive Value of Canned Foods. XVII. Pyridoxine, Biotin and "Folic Acid."* J. Nutrition 31, 347-353, 1946.

Ives, M., Wagner, J. R., Elvehjem, C. A. and Strong, F. M. *The Nutritive Value of Canned Foods. III. Thiamine and Niacin.* J. Nutrition 28, 117-121, 1944.

Ives, M., Zepplin, M., Ames, S. R., Strong, F. M. and Elvehjem, C. A. *The Nutritive Value of Canned Foods. X. Further Studies on Riboflavin, Niacin, and Pantothenic Acid.* J. Am. Dietet. Assoc. 21, 357-359, 1945.

Johnston, F. B. *Vitamin C Fortification of Apple Juice.* Fruit Products J. 22, 195-197, 1943.

Johnstone, W. M. *The Vitamin C Content of Citrus Fruit and Vegetable Juices.* Canadian Hospital 17, No. 6, 22-25, 1940.

Joslyn, M. A. *Retaining Flavor and Vitamin Content in Fruit Juices.* Fruit Products J. 16, 234-236, 1937.

Kohman, E. F., Eddy, W. H., White, M. E. and Sanborn, N. H. *Comparative Experiments with Canned, Home Cooked and Raw Food Diets.* J. Nutrition 14, 9-19, 1937.

Kohman, E. F., Eddy, W. H., White, M. E. and Sanborn, N. H. *The Antirachitic Effect of Some Foods.* Food Research 3, 373-381, 1938.

Knott, E. M. *Thiamine Content of Milk in Relation to Vitamin B_1 Requirement of Infants.* Am. J. Pub. Health 32, 1013-1017, 1942.

Kramer, A. *The Nutritive Value of Canned Foods. VIII. Distribution of Proximate and Mineral Nutrients in the Drained and Liquid Portions of Canned Vegetables.* J. Am. Dietet. Assoc. 21, 354-356, 1945.

Kramer, A. *Nutritive Value of Canned Foods. XVI. Proximate and Mineral Composition.* Food Research 11, 391-398, 1946.

Kramer, A. and Smith, M. H. *Nutritive Value of Canned Foods. XXIV. Effect of Duration and Temperature of Blanch on Proximate and Mineral Composition of Certain Vegetables.* Ind. Eng. Chem. 39, 1007-1009, 1947.

Krieger, C. H. and Scott, H. T. *Stability of Vitamin D in Irradiated Evaporated Milk.* Food Research 3, 283-286, 1938.

Lamb, F. C. *Nutritive Value of Canned Foods. XIX. Factors Affecting Ascorbic Acid Content of Canned Grapefruit and Orange Juices.* Ind. Eng. Chem. 38, 860-864, 1946.

Lamb, F. C., Lewis, L. D. and Lee, S. K. *Effect of Blanching on Retention of Ascorbic Acid and Thiamine in Peas.* Western Canner and Packer **40**, No. 6, 60-62, 1948.

Lamb, F. C., Pressley, A. and Zuch, T. *Nutritive Value of Canned Foods. XXI. Retention of Nutrients During Commercial Production of Various Canned Fruits and Vegetables.* Food Research **12**, 273-288, 1947.

Lanford, C. S., Finkelstein, B. and Sherman, H. C. *Riboflavin Contents of Some Typical Fruits.* J. Nutrition **21**, 175-177, 1941.

Lopez-Matas, A. and Fellers, C. R. *Composition and Nutritive Value of Fresh, Cooked, and Processed Swordfish.* Food Research **13**, 387-396, 1948.

MacGillivray, J. H., Morgan, A. F., Hanna, G. C. and Shultis, A. *Food Values on a Pound Acre and Man-Hour Basis for California Processed Vegetables.* Calif. Agr. Expt. Sta. Bull. No. 8563, 15, 1943.

Maclinn, W. A. and Fellers, C. R. *Ascorbic Acid (Vitamin C) in Tomatoes and Tomato Products.* Mass. Agr. Expt. Sta. Bull. No. 354, 1938.

Mahoney, C. H., Walls, E. P., Hunter, H. A. and Scott, L. E. *Vitamin Content of Peas. Effect of Freezing, Canning and Dehydration.* Ind. Eng. Chem. **38**, 654-657, 1946.

Marshall, R. E. and Robertson, W. F. *XXX. The Nutritive Value of Canned Foods. I. Handling and Storage Procedures for Vegetables Prior to Canning.* Food Technology **2**, 133-143, 1948.

Mayfield, H. L. and Richardson, J. E. *The Vitamin Content of Green String Beans When Cooked or Canned and Stored.* Mont. State College Agr. Expt. Sta. Bull. No. 373, 3-13, 1939.

McConnell, J. E. W., Esselen, W. B. Jr. and Guggenberg, N. *The Effect of Storage Conditions and Type of Container on the Stability of Carotene in Canned Vegetables.* Fruit Products J. **24**, 133-135, 1945.

McElroy, O. E. and Munsell, H. E. *Ascorbic Acid Content of Commercially Canned Tomatoes and Tomato Juice.* J. Am. Med. Asso. **111**, 2138-2139, 1938.

Merritt, K. K. *Feeding the Normal Infant and Child.* J. Am. Dietet. Assoc. **14**, 264-268, 1938.

Meulmans, O. and de Haas, J. H. *Vitamin A, Carotene and Vitamin C Contents of Canned Milk.* Am. J. Diseases Children **56**, 14-21, 1938.

Mickelsen, O., Waisman, H. A. and Elvehjem, C. A. *The Distribution of Vitamin B_1 (Thiamin) in Meat and Meat Products.* J. Nutrition **17**, 269-280, 1939.

Mickelsen, O., Waisman, H. A. and Elvehjem, C. A. *The Distribution of Riboflavin in Meat and Meat Products.* J. Nutrition **18**, 517-526, 1939.

Millares, R. and Fellers, C. R. *Vitamin and Amino Acid Content of Processed Chicken Meat Products.* Food Research **14**, 131-143, 1949.

Monroe, K. H., Brighton, K. W. and Bendix, G. H. *The Nutritive Value of Canned Foods. XXVIII. Some Studies of Commercial Warehouse Temperatures with Reference to the Stability of Vitamins in Canned Foods.* Food Technology **3**, 292-299, 1949.

Moore, E. L., Wiederhold, E. and Atkins, C. D. *Changes Occurring in Orange and Grapefruit Juices During Commercial Processing and Subsequent Storage of the Glass and Tin Packed Products.* Fruit Products J. **23**, 270-275, 285, 1944.

Moore, E. L., Wiederhold, E. and Atkins, C. D. *Ascorbic Acid Retention in Florida Grapefruit Juices. II. During Storage of the Canned Products.* Canner **100**, No. 8, 55-57, 1945.

Moore, E. L., Wiederhold, E., Atkins, C. D. and MacDowell, L. G. *Ascorbic Acid Retention in Florida Grapefruit Juices. I. During Commercial Canning.* Canner **98**, No. 9, 24-26, 1944.

Moschette, D. S., Hinman, W. F. and Halliday, E. G. *Nutritive Value of Canned Foods. XXII. Effect of Time and Temperature of Storage on Vitamin Content of Commercially Canned Fruits and Fruit Juices. (Stored 12 Months.)* Ind. Eng. Chem. **39**, 994-999, 1947.

Newman, K. R. and Fellers, C. R. *Vitamin C in Packaged Foods Purchased in Retail Markets.* J. Am. Dietet. Assoc. **16**, 695-696, 1940.

Neilands, J. B., Sirny, R. J., Sohjell, I., Strong, F. M. and Elvehjem, C. A. *XXXIII. The Nutritive Value of Canned Foods. II. Amino Acid Content of Fish and Meat Products.* J. Nutrition **39**, 187-202, 1949.

Neilands, J. B., Strong, F. M. and Elvehjem, C. A. *The Nutritive Value of Canned Foods. XXV. Vitamin Content of Canned Fish Products.* J. Nutrition **34**, 633-643, 1947.

Paul, P., Einbecker, B., Kelley, L., Jackson, M., Jackson, L., Marshall, R. E., Robertson, W. F. and Ohlson, M. A. *XXXII. The Nutritive Value of Canned Foods. II. Changes in Ascorbic Acid of Vegetables During Storage Prior to Canning.* Food Technology **3**, 228-231, 1949.

Pederson, C. S. *Relation Between Quality and Chemical Composition of Canned Sauerkraut.* N. Y. State Agr. Expt. Sta. Bull. No. 693, 1940.

Pederson, C. S. and Beattie, H. G. *Effect of Processing and Storage on the Quality and Ascorbic Acid Content of Sauerkraut.* Food Packer **27**, No. 8, 44, 46, 48, 78, 1946.

Pederson, C. S., Mack, G. L. and Athawes, W. L. *Vitamin C Content of Sauerkraut.* Food Research **4**, 31-45, 1939.

Pett, L. B. and Cantor, M. M. *The Nutritive Value of Canned Foods.* Canada Med. Assoc. J. **40**, 174-177, 1939.

Poe, C. F. *Vitamin B_1 Content of Colorado Commercially Canned Tomato Juices.* Univ. of Colorado Studies Ser. **D2**, No. 1, 1-16, 1943.

Poe, C. F. *Vitamin B_2 Content of Colorado Commercially Canned Tomato Juices.* Univ. of Colorado Studies Ser. **D2**, No. 1, 7-12, 1943.

Poe, C. F., Gant, O. K. and Griffin, E. *The Vitamin A Content of Some Commercially Canned Tomato Juice.* Fruit Products J. **19**, 73-74, 88, 1939.

Poe, C. F. and McGuire, E. G. *The Vitamin B₁ Content of Commercially Canned Tomato Juices.* Fruit Products J. **21**, 108-109, 1941.

Poe, C. F. and McGuire, E. G. *A Comparison of the Vitamin B₁ Content of Home Canned and Commercially Canned Tomato Juices.* Fruit Products J. **24**, 200-201, 217, 1945.

Poling, C. E., Schultz, H. W. and Robinson, H. E. *The Retention of the Nutritive Quality of Beef and Pork Muscle Proteins During Dehydration, Canning, Roasting, and Frying.* J. Nutrition **27**, 23-34, 1944.

Poole, M. W., Hamil, B. M., Cooley, T. B. and Macy, I. G. *Addition of Vegetable Soup and Strained Vegetables to Diet of Artificially Fed Infants.* Am. J. Diseases Children **55**, 1158, 1938.

Porter, T., Wharton, M. A., Bennett, B. B., Brewer, W. D. and Kelley, A. L. *Processed Green Beans.* J. Am. Dietet. Assoc. **22**, 1084-1087, 1946.

Pressley, A., Ridder, C., Smith, M. C. and Caldwell, E. *The Nutritive Value of Canned Foods. II. Ascorbic Acid and Carotene or Vitamin A Content.* J. Nutrition **28**, 107-116, 1948.

Pugsley, L. I. *Nutritive Value of Marine Products. XV. Proximate Analyses of Canned British Columbia Crabs, Shrimps and Clams.* J. Fisheries Res. Board Can. **5**, 344-346, 1941.

Pugsley, L. I., Wills, G. and D'Aoust, T. *The Vitamin A Activity and Carotene Content of Tomato Juice.* Can. J. Res. **25E**, 162-166, 1947.

Quinones, V. L., Guerrant, N. B. and Dutcher, R. A. *Vitamin Content of Some Tropical Fruits, Their Juices and Nectars.* Food Research **9**, 415-417, 1944.

Reedman, E. J. and Buckby, L. *The Vitamin B₁ Content of Canned Pork.* Can. J. Res. **21C**, 261-266, 1943.

Rice, E. E. and Robinson, H. E. *Nutritive Value of Canned and Dehydrated Meat and Meat Products.* Am. J. Pub. Health **34**, 587-592, 1944.

Roberts, J. A. *Vitamin C in Citrus Juice Beverages and Canned Grapefruit Juice.* Food Research **2**, 331-337, 1937.

Robinson, W. B., Moyer, J. C. and Kertesz, Z. I. *"Thermal Maceration" of Plant Tissue.* Plant Physiology **24**, 317-319, 1949.

Robinson, W. B., Stotz, E. and Kertesz, Z. I. *The Effect of Manufacturing Methods on the Ascorbic Acid Content and Consistency Characteristics of Tomato Juice.* J. Nutrition **30**, 435-442, 1945.

Rose, M. C. and Phipard, E. H. F. *Vitamins B and G Values of Peas and Lima Beans Under Various Conditions.* J. Nutrition **14**, 55-67, 1937.

Ross, E. *Effect of Time and Temperature of Storage on Vitamin C Retention in Canned Citrus Juices.* Food Research 9, 27-33, 1944.

Russell, W. C., Taylor, M. W. and Beuk, J. F. *The Nicotinic Acid Content of Some Common Fruits and Vegetables as Prepared for Human Consumption.* J. Nutrition 25, 275-284, 1943.

Sale, J. W. *et al.* *Ascorbic Acid in Tomatoes and Tomato Juice.* J. Assoc. Offic. Agr. Chem. 29, 69-75, 1946.

Sale, J. W. *et al.* *Ascorbic Acid in Grapefruit Juice, Orange Juice and Their Blends.* J. Assoc. Offic. Agr. Chem. 30, 673-680, 1947.

Schultz, F. W. and Knott, E. M. *Factors Affecting the Vitamin B_1 Content of Evaporated Milk.* Proc. Soc. Expt. Biol. Med. 40, 532-535, 1939.

Scott, L. E. and Walls, E. P. *Ascorbic Acid Content and Sugar-Acid Ratios of Fresh Fruit and Processed Juice of Tomato Varieties.* Proc. Am. Soc. Hort. Sci. 50, 269-272, 1947.

Scoular, F. I. and Willard, H. *Effect of Refrigeration on Ascorbic Acid Content of Canned Juices after Opening.* J. Am. Dietet. Assoc. 20, 223-225, 1944.

Sheft, B. B., Griswold, R. M., Tarlowsky, E. and Halliday, E. G. *Nutritive Value of Canned Foods. XXVI. Effect of Time and Temperature of Storage on Vitamin Content of Commercially Canned Fruits and Fruit Juices. (Stored 18 and 24 Months.)* Ind. Eng. Chem. 41, 144-145, 1949.

Smith, H. R. and Smith, K. R. *Effect of Freezing on the Utilization of Canned Foods.* Food Research 9, 66-75, 1944.

Smith, M. C. *The Vitamin C Content of Commercially Canned Fruit and Vegetable Juices.* Ariz. Agr. Expt. Sta. Ann. Rept. 55, 64, 1944.

Souders, H. J., Hunscher, H. A., Hummel, F. C. and Macy, I. G. *Influence of Fluid and of Evaporated Milk on Mineral and Nitrogen Metabolism of Growing Children.* Am. J. Diseases Children 58, 529-539, 1939.

Steers, A. W. and Fischer, L. *Comparative Study of Vitamins and Constants of Free and Extracted Oils from Canned Sockeye Salmon.* J. Am. Pharm. Assoc. 29, 166-170, 1940.

Stewart, A. P. Jr. and Sharp, P. F. *Vitamin C Content of Market Milk, Evaporated Milk, and Powdered Whole Milk.* J. Nutrition 31, 161-173, 1946.

Swanson, P. P., Stevenson, G. and Nelson, P. M. *Effect of Storage on Vitamin A Content of Canned Tomatoes.* J. Home Econ. 32, 246-251, 1940.

Theriault, F. R. and Fellers, C. R. *Effect of Freezing and of Canning in Glass and Tin on the Available Iron Content of Foods.* Food Research 7, 503-508, 1942.

Thompson, M. L., Cunningham, E. and Snell, E. E. *The Nutritive Value of Canned Foods. IV. Riboflavin and Pantothenic Acid.* J. Nutrition 28, 123-129, 1944.

Tripp, F., Satterfield, G. H. and Holmes, A. D. *Varietal Differences in the Vitamin C (Ascorbic Acid) Content of Tomatoes.* J. Home Econ. **29**, 258-262, 1937

Vavich, M. G., Stern, R. M. and Guerrant, N. B. *Nutritive Value of Canned Foods. XII. Determination of Ascorbic Acid of Fresh Green Peas.* Ind. Eng. Chem., Anal. Ed. **17**, 531, 1945.

Wagner, J. R., Ives, M., Strong, F. M. and Elvehjem, C. A. *The Nutritive Value of Canned Foods. VII. Effect of Commercial Canning and Short-Time Storage on Ascorbic Acid Content of Grapefruit Juice.* Food Research **10**, 469-475, 1945.

Wagner, J. R., Strong, F. M. and Elvehjem, C. A. *Nutritive Value of Canned Foods. XIV. Effect of Commercial Canning Operations on the Ascorbic Acid, Thiamine, Riboflavin and Niacin Contents of Vegetables.* Ind. Eng. Chem. **39**, 985-990, 1947.

Wagner, J. R., Strong, F. M. and Elvehjem, C. A. *Nutritive Value of Canned Foods. XV. Effects of Blanching on the Retention of Ascorbic Acid, Thiamine, and Niacin in Vegetables.* Ind. Eng. Chem. **39**, 990-993, 1947.

Wiederhold, E., Atkins, C. D. and Moore, E. L. *Ascorbic Acid Retention in Florida Grapefruit Juices. III. As Related to Individual Factors of Canning Plant Operations.* Canner **100**, No. 23, 12-14, 23, 1945.

Woessner, W. W., Elvehjem, C. A. and Schuette, H. A. *The Determination of Ascorbic Acid in Evaporated Milk, Powdered Milk and Powdered Milk Products.* J. Nutrition **20**, 327-338, 1940.

Compilations and Reviews

Ascorbic Acid in Canned Citrus Juices. Nutrition Revs. **2**, 306-307, 1944.

Baby's First Fruits and Vegetables. Hygeia **17**, 171-172, 1939.

Booher, L. E., Hartzler, E. R. and Hewston, E. M. *A Compilation of the Vitamin Values of Foods in Relation to Processing and Other Variants.* U. S. Dept. Agr. Circ. No. 638, 1, 1942.

Booher, L. E. and Marsh, R. L. *The Vitamin A Values of 128 Foods as Determined by the Rat-Growth Method.* U. S. Dept. Agr. Tech. Bull. No. 802, 1941.

Cameron, E. J., Pilcher, R. W. and Clifcorn, L. E. *Nutrient Retention During Canned Food Production.* Am. J. Pub. Health **39**, 756-763, 1949.

Chatfield, C. and Adams, G. *Proximate Composition of American Food Materials.* U. S. Dept. Agr. Circ. No. 549, 1940.

Clifcorn, L. E. *Variables Influencing Vitamin Content of Processed Foods.* Food Packer **26**, No. 9, 46-48, 1945.

Clifcorn, L. E. *Factors Influencing Vitamin Content of Canned Foods.* Advances in Food Research, Vol. I, 39-104, New York, Academic Press, Inc., 1948.

Clouse, R. C. *Compilation of Recent Data on Mineral and Vitamin Values of Foods.* J. Am. Dietet. Assoc. **18**, 553-561, 1942.

Clouse, R. C. *Compilation of Recent Data on Mineral and Vitamin Values of Foods.* J. Am. Dietet. Assoc. **19**, 496; 19, 746-755, 1943.

Eichelberger, M. *The Importance of Economical Milk in Human Nutrition.* Am. J. Pub. Health **30**, 169-174, 1940.

Elvehjem, C. A. *Vitamins and Food Processing.* Agr. Eng. **26**, No. 1, 12, 15, 1945.

Feaster, J. F. *Nutritive Values of Canned Fruits and Vegetables.* Am. J. Pub. Health **34**, 593-597, 1944.

Feaster, J. F., Tompkins, M. D. and Pearce, W. E. *Effect of Storage on Vitamins and Quality in Canned Foods.* Food Research **14**, 25-39, 1949.

Fellers, C. R. *Effect of Processing on the Vitamin A (Carotene) Content of Foods.* Proc. First Food Conference, Inst. Food Technologists, 97-107, 1940.

Fixen, M. A. B. *The Vitamin Content of Human Foods as Affected by Processes of Cooking and Canning (With Tables).* Nutrition Abstracts & Revs. **8**, 281-295, 1938.

Food Processing and Nutritive Value. Nutrition Revs. **7**, 284-286, 1949.

Hallman, G. V. and Clifcorn, L. E. *Canned Meats: Their Nutritive Properties.* Food Manufacturer **14**, 273-277, 1939.

Harris, R. S., Proctor, B. E., Goldblith, S. and Brody, J. *Effect of Processing on the Vitamin B_1 Content of Foods.* Proc. First Food Conferences, Inst. Food Technologists, 109-121, 1940.

Jackson, J. M., Feaster, J. F. and Pilcher, R. W. *The Effect of Canning Procedures on Vitamins in Foods.* Proc. Inst. Food Tech. 81-90, 1945.

King, C. G. and Tressler, D. K. *Effect of Processing on the Vitamin C Content of Foods.* Proc. First Food Conference, Inst. Food Technologists, 123-132, 1940.

Kohman, E. F. *Vitamins in Canned Foods.* Bull. 19-L, 4th Rev. National Canners Association, Washington, D. C., 1937.

Kohman, E. F. *The Preservation of the Nutritive Value of Foods in Processing, Handbook of Nutrition XV.* J. Am. Med. Assoc. **120**, 831-838, 1942.

Kohman, E. F., Eddy, W. H., White, M. E. and Sanborn, N. H. *Nutritive Value of Canned Foods Revealed.* Western Canner and Packer **29**, No. 9, 19, 1937.

Morgan, A. F. *Comparative Nutritive Values of Vegetables.* Fruit Products J. **23**, 334-337, 1944.

Nutritional Quality of Processed Foods. Nutrition Revs. **2**, 336-338, 1944.

Nutritive Value of Canned Foods. Part I. Nutrition Revs. **7**, 142-144, 1949.

Nutritive Value of Canned Foods. Part II. Nutrition Revs. 7, 144-146, 1949.

Pilcher, R. W. *Vitamin Content of Canned Foods.* The Canning Trade 67, No. 41, 12, 14, 1945.

Pilcher, R. W. and Clark, B. S. *Current Trends in Nutrition Research in Canned Foods.* Am. J. Pub. Health 37, 702-708, 1947.

Tables of Food Composition in Terms of Eleven Nutrients. U. S. Dept. Agr. Misc. Pub. No. 572, 1945.

Vail, G. E. *The Effect of Processing Upon the Nutritive Value of Food.* J. Am. Dietet. Assoc. 18, 569-574, 1942.

INDEX